D0064867

THE BIG ONE,
THE BLACK ONE,
THE FAT ONE
AND THE OTHER ONE

My Life in Showbiz
WILLIAM DONALDSON

MICHAEL O'MARA BOOKS LIMITED

First published in *The Independent* as a weekly column.

Published in book form in 1992 in Great Britain by
Michael O'Mara Books Limited,
9 Lion Yard, Tremadoc Road,
London SW4 7NQ

A CIP catalogue record of this book is available from the British Library.

ISBN 1–85479–147–8

Typeset by Florencetype Limited, Kewstoke, Avon
Printed and bound in England by Richard Clay, Bungay, Suffolk

Banks, Bail and the Haute Bohème

Currently I'm giving all my money to a sweet girl called Alison. She has a demure mouth and unconsoling eyes and when I buy her a Porsche or an apartment she smiles a little private smile and says: 'Thank you ever so much.'

She is very respectable. She has a brother and a horse and she gives dinner parties, and the thought of her presiding importantly at these breaks my heart. I've just made her my literary agent. She's excellent, though there was a slight confusion the first time she negotiated on my behalf. The Editor of the *Independent* rang up to make a deal, explaining that I'd given him Alison's number.

'Do you want to see me?' she said.

'No,' he said. 'I just want to talk.'

'That will be extra,' she said.

Last week she arrived late for a meeting with the Head of Light Entertainment at the BBC, who is showing some interest in my TV development, *Root Into Europe*. He gave us a beefy lecture on the art of comedy and then he said:

'Who should play Root? Nigel Havers, do you think?'

My literary agent stood up. 'This man's an imbecile,' she said. 'Come along, Mr Bear.'

Later, on the way home, I told her that the *haute bohème* had assembled the night before in the old-time room at Claridges to honour J.P. Donleavy on his sixtieth birthday. She was silent for a while and then she said:

'Do you have to be a certain age to be a bohemian or what?'

Dear God, I love my literary agent. Be that as it may, my bank manager has called in my overdraft, even though I haven't got one, and it seems that my idea for *Root Into Europe* is already owned by Robert Bolt's butler. I blame Alison, in fact. Some weeks ago, she took off to Paris with an American. I could have handled this, but she sent me a postcard saying: 'Having a wonderful time – hardly been on my feet since we arrived,' which depressed me badly.

On the day I received this, I dined with the Robert Bolts and was surprised to discover that my old friend Tankybums, with whom I used to shrimp in Broadstairs, had become their butler. I sat through dinner in a fog of misery at my literary agent Alison's behaviour and over coffee sold Tankybums the television rights in all my books.

Now his solicitor has written to say that whatever my idea for a television series is, it almost certainly belongs not to me but to Tankybums. I could shaft Tankybums, I suppose, but it's hard to shaft a man you've shrimped with. Alternatively, I could accommodate him somehow, introduce him as my partner, but he's too tall, and he has a small dog and he looks as if he lives in Brighton.

I was wondering what to do about this when my literary agent, Alison, telephoned to ask me whether I'd stand bail for her brother who had been arrested in a drugs swoop. I enjoy standing bail, as it happens, and I'm rather good at it. I have a special suit to do it in and I always wear my Old Wykehamist tie. I went, as requested, to Horseferry Road Magistrates Court where I was shortly in the box, being quizzed as to whether I was good for the £5000 surety the magistrate was seeking. I said I was a writer, whereupon the magistrate drew back and looked at me warily as if I was a bomb in a handbag. He reminded me that writing is a hazardous business and then he said I could lose my house.

'I haven't got a house,' I said.

The magistrate was thunderstruck. 'You haven't got a *house*?' he said. 'Where on earth do you live?'

Shortly in a cardboard box, I said, unless I could persuade my wife that my literary agent, Alison – whom I loved with all my money – was a fiction. Eventually, the magistrate ruled that he could only accept my surety if my bank would guarantee it.

There was nothing for it but to break the first rule of satisfactory banking, which is never to meet the manager. If you're just a blip on a computer screen you could be up to anything. You could have a job, or you could be one of those young men ahead of you in the queue who deposit great sackfuls of money, but if the manager meets you he can see you've had it. I was feeling confident, however, in my court suit and Old Wykehamist tie, so I went straight to the bank. The manager turned out to be a nice young man, but when I said I was a writer he looked unhappy.

'Oh – you're a writer, are you?'

'A writer? Goodness no. I'm a television producer. Currently three serious players in the game are fighting over a concept of mine: Paul Jackson, who wears red braces and is usually on the other line; Mark Chapman – you saw *Wax in Moscow*, I expect? – and a fellow from the north who wears a ginger wig and an earring. I'm not very impressed by him. Oh, and Tankybums.'

'Who's Tankybums?' asked the manager.

'Robert Bolt's butler,' I said. 'He owns the idea.'

'What are you going to do about that?'

'Shaft him,' I said.

This sounded suitably red-blooded, I thought, Thatcherite, even, but my bank manager looked doubtful.

'Oh dear,' he said. 'Why?'

'He's too tall,' I said, 'and he has a small dog and the one in the ginger wig would laugh at him.'

'But you don't like the one in the ginger wig.'

'That's true.'

'It sounds as if you're in a bit of a muddle.'

'Certainly not,' I said. 'And the best news is that I have this red-hot new agent. You have to get up very early in the morning not to catch my literary agent on the job.'

The manager looked impressed and then he asked me why I was here. I explained that my new agent's brother was up on a drugs charge and that the magistrate would only allow me to stand bail if the bank would guarantee it.

'I see,' said the manager. 'Do you have a house?'

This question was beginning to irritate me, so I replied, rather crossly, that no, I didn't have a fucking house, and this was when my bank manager called in my overdraft, even though I didn't have one. When I telephoned my literary agent, Alison, with the bad news she said that it was quite all right, she had never had any faith in me and that she had arranged for Roscoe to stand bail.

'Who's Roscoe?' I said.

'My American,' she said. 'The one I go to Paris with. *He's* got a house.'

Over lunch today, I was recounting all this to my friend Michael O'Mara, the brilliant young American publisher. My mistake, he said, had been to wear my Old Wykehamist tie, and then he told me a curious story. When he was just starting in publishing, he said, the board of the company he worked for engaged as Sales Director a man who, in O'Mara's opinion, was an obvious conman. O'Mara expressed his doubts to the board about the man's background, but the Managing Director suggested haughtily that O'Mara, as an American, was hardly a judge in these matters.

Sure enough, the Sales Director disappeared after a few weeks with all the takings.

'Well done,' I said. 'You twigged him. All bogus, his background?'

'Oh no,' O'Mara said. 'He'd been to Winchester.'

I don't understand this.

A Pasta with Pratley

Every six months or so, I agree to have dinner with Pratley. I don't enjoy it, but we were colleagues in the sixties – friends almost – and it's nice for him to see me from time to time. He was in the recording business once, I think – selling cover versions of top ten hits to W.H. Smith, or something of the sort – but he lost his nerve in 1971 and what he has been doing since I wouldn't know.

He's quite practical, the sort of man who has a workroom, and I think he may for twenty years have been inventing things – without success – may, with his own hands, have built an extension to his house, allowing him to rent a floor to students. He has a failed wife and two children, one of whom is almost certainly a nurse and one of whom may not be.

I give him an hour and a half when we meet and, to make it clear that I can't waste time, I insist in eating in a fast-food pasta bar. It's heavy going, the nearest I come to social work, but I always feel better afterwards, rather as my mother must have felt after she'd flogged off to visit an old retainer – a chauffeur, a nanny or a parlourmaid – in a retirement home.

On Tuesday, Pratley showed irritating signs of wanting to talk about himself.

'Since we last met,' he said, 'things have improved. For some time now I've been visiting a girl in the afternoon.'

I couldn't be bothered with that, of course, so I brought him up to date with the exciting things happening in my life.

'You will be interested to hear,' I said, 'that I'm developing a TV series with Mark Chapman, the immensely gifted director of *Wax on Wheels*.'

'Oh – so you're still writing, then,' said Pratley.

This is the sort of thing I have to put up with, but I don't mind too much. If it makes him feel better to pull me down to his level, so be it. I can afford to be generous.

I let that pass and told him about the Bollomsballs Fund – organized by myself to help Val Hennessey who is being sued by a Soho barman – and my plans to filch from it enough to take my literary agent, Alison, for a holiday in Ibiza.

Pratley looked a little shocked, so I explained that my solicitor had drawn up the fund's articles in such a way as to allow the trustees – myself, Honest John and Jillypoo – a certain latitude. This wasn't quite true, in fact; it's the sort of thing I say to Pratley simply to agitate him, to make him see that life at the dangerous edge of things is the only one worth living.

To my surprise he now started to babble on about this girl of his. 'I give her £20 and stay for half an hour,' he said.

I could see it all: a mean room on the second floor; a queue on the stairs, perhaps; a bruised girl with broken hair; an electric fire with one bar working and a television set with a coathanger as an aerial flickering on and off during the sad act of damp relief.

To punish him, to make him understand what he could never have – not for £20, at least – I now showed him a photograph of Alison, looking so sweet, so graceful and demure in the little Katharine Hamnett skirt I bought her for my birthday.

'She's very pretty,' he said. 'Perhaps we could all go out together.'

I was thunderstruck. Could he really think I would introduce

5

her to a man who looked as if he had, with his own hands, built an extension to his house?

It's odd, really. We're about the same age, Pratley and I, but I'm still welcome where the music is, move in the early p.m. with nonchalance below the waist, get invited to Blues Brothers parties by thirty-five-year-olds who once knew Tina Brown at Oxford and now have a comic novel pending, whereas he's definitely had it. To my surprise, he was still burbling on about this girl he visits in the afternoon, so I cut him short.

'You'll want to know how I met Alison,' I said. 'Melanie introduced us.'

'Who's Melanie?' he said.

Sometimes you wonder if it's all worthwhile. 'If you had had the common courtesy to read my excellent novel *Is This Allowed*?' I said, 'you'd know that, with Melanie, I lived at a pitch of enthralled danger attained by very few men. She had enchanting qualities so I gave her free-base cocaine and my wife's savings, and then she left me.'

Talking about Melanie to Pratley, who, poor man, would never have experienced anything so lovely, seemed a kind of blasphemy.

'What happened to her?' he said.

'I often wonder,' I said. 'She was cured by cold-eyed Christians in an addiction centre. She was last heard of living in Newcastle with a gardener.'

'Newcastle?' said Pratley. 'How strange. What did you say her name was?'

'Melanie.'

'Are you quite sure she isn't back in London?'

'For her sake, I hope not,' I said. 'In London she'd be on the game, seeing fat men like you in the afternoon – and she was so beautiful, so brave.'

'My girl,' said Pratley, 'the one I was telling you about, asked me for £300 last week to finance a cocaine deal. She wanted to go to Newcastle where she had a friend, she said. Shall I tell you her name?'

'Okay,' I said. I wasn't in the least interested, but it seemed polite to pretend I was.

'Tracey,' said Pratley.

6

An Imitation Woman

I am still trying to work out why the *Sunday Times* rejected me as a fit subject for their 'A Life in the Day of' column. My mistake, I think, was to tell their crisp reporter that I had recently become an addict. I was only trying to be helpful, but I had forgotten how easily shocked young people are these days.

I apologised for alarming her and explained that, like all addicts, I have two sorts of day: those when my drug is readily available and those when it isn't. In either case, I said, I wake up in a cold terror which I try to escape by moving faster than myself, by jumping out of my skin, as it were. I rocket from my bed and spin in tiny maddened circles like a dog that's sat on a thistle. Sometimes I fall over, but usually I manage to make myself a cup of coffee. Then, for the rest of the day, I think about my dealer.

'That's it, really. Cheerio. Do I get to see a proof?'

'Just a minute,' said the crisp reporter. 'Who's your dealer?'

'My literary agent, Alison.'

'What does she sell you?'

'An imitation woman. A performance. We satirize reality like Nicola Six and Keith . . .'

'Who are they? Friends of yours?'

'Acquaintances,' I said. 'Addicts don't have friends. It's entirely inauthentic what we do, quite unreal and therefore imperishable. That's the point of it. Trying to cheat death, do you see? If it's a really bad day it's because I haven't slept – and that's because my dealer has a clever new trick.

'When she's going to withdraw my supply for a day or two she says: "Don't worry, I'll phone you on Sunday." I cancel every-thing, switch off the answering machine and stare at the tele-phone, defying it not to ring. She doesn't call, but Pratley does. This is Pratley's chance.'

'Who is Pratley?' asked the crisp reporter.

'Pratley is everyone I've been trying to shake off for twenty years: old men whose telephonic manner is wheedling yet defiant, who start with a joke or a funny voice. It had never occurred to me that I might be someone's Pratley, but the possibility has recently crossed my mind. I have discovered that I

7

can, literally, make people cry with boredom.

'There are only three people now, apart from my dealer, whom I can bear to see: my best friend Little Jo, Susan Carr and Mark Chapman, the richly gifted young director with whom I am developing a television series. Meetings with them have been a kind of methadone maintenance treatment.

'Last week, however, Mark Chapman fell sound asleep while I was in mid-anecdote and now when I phone he pretends to be making a film with Ruby Wax, if you please; Susan Carr has cancelled our last four lunches; and yesterday I had spent a mere two hours explaining quite a simple point to Little Jo when I noticed that tears were pouring down her cheeks. "I'm sorry," she said. "but I can't take any more of this. I'm off."'

'Extraordinary,' said the crisp reporter.

'Precisely. Anyway, I tell Pratley to pig off out of it and I try to distract myself by watching television, preferably American football. It doesn't work. An intelligent woman like you will find this hard to credit, but even the exhilarating spectacle of a coked-up line-backer driving a quarter-back head-first into the floor can't take my mind off the heavy, dreadful fact that my dealer hasn't rung.

'I go to bed and toss and turn with a pain like dysentery. "Someone else drowned in that lash-wide stare/And me supposed to be ignorant/or find it funny, or not to care." Larkin, do you see? Wake up!'

'Sorry. Is it always as bad as that?'

'By no means. On good days, on days when I'm due for a fix, I'm the happiest man in the developed world. I feel sorry for anyone who isn't me. I'm so happy I can't sit down.

'I'm an hour early at our rendez-vous, often a restaurant I'd not be seen dead in as a rule. With her, I'd go to Le Gavroche. With her, I'd go to Royal Ascot, into a pub, to Ireland, to a literary lunch, to a christening or a cocktail party. I'd go to the *opera* with her, I tell you! (I wouldn't see *Aspects of Love*, of course – I'm trying to keep this serious.)

'When she walks in I almost faint with happiness. Once did. Once passed clean out at Bibendum. Recovered consciousness to discover that she'd availed herself of this opportunity to have an early night. Normally I blast her with adoration. It must be terrifying, like having the door of a furnace suddenly opened on you – to borrow an analogy due to Lady Longford, I rather think. "You're perfect," I say. "I can't live without you." "Thank you ever so much," she says. "By the way, I'm off to Los Angeles next week with my American."

'I recoil as if shot, sometimes falling backwards off my chair. "Don't worry," she says, "I'll phone you on Sunday." She won't off course, but Pratley will. Not a bad life, I think you'll agree. Better than reality.'

'We'll let you know,' the crisp reporter said.

Blown Out by Wogan

Writing last Saturday about my sad addiction, I may have given less credit than I should have done to the many kind people who have tried to help me. Of these I owe most, perhaps, to Mark Chapman – a point he made most vigorously himself when I saw him on Monday morning.

It is certainly the case that had I, for the past few weeks, not been able to pitch up at his office where we are working together on my television development, *Root Into Europe*, things would have been very much worse.

I wouldn't normally recommend an office as a cure for anything, but when I say that Chapman's office is unique I know what I'm talking about, believe me. I've worked in an office before, once did two days in advertising (more accurately, the same day twice) and, when I left this occupation, I vowed I'd never seek another like it. (It was touch and go, I must admit, when I became the *Mail on Sunday*'s gossip columnist. Fortunately, they forgot to provide me with a desk, so I ran my department – interviewing my sources, wrecking marriages, filing scoops and so forth – from a telephone kiosk in Bouverie Street, and, because Sir David English couldn't find me, I continued to work from my kiosk for six months after I was fired.)

Be that as it may, Chapman's office is, as I say, unique, staffed by the most delightful people you could meet in a long day's march. Each is sweeter and saner than the next, each does his or her job brilliantly and menaces no one else.

9

Chapman is the cat's whiskers, as is his partner Paul Sommers; my new best friend Justin Judd (just to me, Mr Judd to you) is the pick of the bunch in my book, but Jeremy – the hottest researcher in the western world – is definitely my favourite, as are Chris and Rachel; and when it comes to Jenny and Catey there are no words adequately to describe their excellence of character and the brilliance with which they carry out their various duties. They could stop making television programmes and, instead, charge punters to come in off the street and bask in their healing company.

That said, Chapman won't mind my admitting on his behalf that he is a trifle vain. I first spotted this when he stopped laughing at my nose jokes. I was baffled at first, but then I noticed that he himself has a nose that a French balladeer would, frankly, give his nose for. His nose should always have a Gauloise under it.

One afternoon last week, he lost his pen – later finding it on his desk.

'It was under my nose,' he said.

'Everything's under your nose,' I said, and he wouldn't speak to me for the rest of the day. I was so upset by this that I had a word with my new best friend, Justin Judd.

'If I tell you a story,' said Judd, 'can I have your solemn promise that it will remain between you, me and the bedpost?'

'Absolutely,' I said.

'Some months ago,' said Judd, 'Chapman was hit in the eye by a boom. It wasn't serious, but the doctor said that he must wear an eye-patch for a while. Chapman refused, arguing that it would spoil his looks. Jenny and Catey tried to persuade him that he'd look very dashing in an eye-patch.

'"I wish I could wear an eye-patch," Jenny said.

'"Nothing's stopping you," Chapman said.

'"All right, I will," Jenny said.

'The next day she came to the office in an eye-patch, but Chapman still refused to wear his. Rachel and Catey said how nice Jenny looked in her eye-patch and how lucky Chapman was that he could wear one too.

'"All right," said Chapman, "*you* wear eye-patches."

'Rachel and Catey obliged, but Chapman still wouldn't wear his. In the end he agreed to put one on if we all did the same. For a week, everyone in the office had to wear an eye-patch.

'One afternoon Seamus Cassidy, Channel 4's brilliant young Commissioning Editor (Entertainment), and his boss, Michael Grade, were due to come into the office to finalize an important deal. Cassidy pitched up first and Rachel, in reception, told him that, out of respect for Chapman's feelings, he had to wear an eye-patch. When Grade arrived he was shown into the board-room where he was confronted by eleven people, including his man Cassidy, all wearing eye-patches. Thinking he was the butt of some childish prank, he walked out and the deal was blown.'

The day after my new best friend Justin Judd told me this story, I went into the office and was surprised to find Ruby Wax wearing a false nose. I'm not going to be caught like Grade, I thought, so I gave it a good tweak.

'Ha! Ha!' I said.

'Ha! Ha!' said Ruby. 'How did you know it was false?'

'Judd told me about Chapman and the eye-patch incident,' I explained. 'What is it this time?'

'His nose,' said Ruby. 'He's just had an inch taken off and we've all got to wear false ones for a while. Here's yours.'

The nuisance is that on Tuesday I was asked to appear on Wogan to promote my startlingly funny new book (*The Soap Letters* by Henry Root) but when I said that I'd be wearing a false nose they blew me out, replacing me with someone called David Icke who probably won't even mention my book.

As Drunk as a Lord

I haven't had a drink for thirty years, which was no disadvantage, I think, when I was wine correspondent of the *Tatler*. Tina Brown, the editor, used to send me great crates of the filth and, having disposed of this elsewhere, I'd write about cricket or chess or current gripes, such as the boring refusal of stuffbag restaurants such as Le Gavroche to play pop music loudly while one ate. Tina didn't notice or, if she did, she didn't seem to mind.

My habitual sobriety caught up with me this week, however, when on the day that I should have seen Dustin Hoffman in *The*

Merchant of Venice I got blotto instead while lunching, under the name of Lord Dynevor, with my ex-secretary Miranda.

Twenty-five years ago Miranda worked for me and Lord Dynevor when we were theatrical producers and I hadn't seen her since she married an Australian in 1964.

We were in love with her, Lord Dynevor and I, but since I was on terms with satirists in those days, wearing an overcoat and taking tea as often as not with Peter Cook and so forth – whereas Lord Dynevor just did a lot of stuff in Welsh – I naturally assumed that I was her favourite. It came as no surprise, therefore, when it was me she telephoned on Tuesday to say that she was in London for a week and to ask me out to lunch.

It came as more of a surprise when I walked into the restaurant and her face hit the floor. I might have recovered from this, but when she asked after my daughters, and then my ulcers, the penny dropped; she thought I was Lord Dynevor. Over the years she'd forgotten which of us was which; she'd preferred him all along and had asked the wrong one out to lunch.

There was nothing for it but to pretend to be him, and that wasn't easy. Lord Dynevor's a gentleman, no one more so, whereas I've become increasingly common, I don't know why. To behave like the King of Wales, which Lord Dynevor would be had the English any sense of historical decorum, takes some doing when you're wearing shoes which would look better on a Spaniard. And, as Lord Dynevor, who likes a glass of wine with his meal, I had to drink. By the time Miranda asked me about me, I was pissed.

'Whatever became of the other one?' she said.

'Donaldson? Off the rails. There was talk of immoral earnings, but I gather, in fact, that for some years he has been *marinero* on a Spanish smack, he and the *capitano* reading to one another on winter nights from the works of Shakespeare, *The Merchant of Venice* being a particular favourite, I gather.'

'Goodness, how sad. Surely he did well from *Beyond the Fringe*?'

'He cheated them, frankly: Cook, Miller, Bennett, the other one. At the start they were on £75 a week each, do you see? Donaldson and Sir Donald Albery were trousering £2000 between them every pay-day.'

'That wasn't fair.'

'Quite so. Miller & Co caught on and wrote politely to the management seeking an adjustment. Albery invited them to tea. Odd situation. The combined IQs of Miller & Co must have touched 1000, whereas Albery and Donaldson would have been lucky to muster 100 between them – to say nothing of the moral disproportion – yet Albery ran rings round them "Difficult times . . . rising costs . . . rates . . . taxes . . . laundry . . . review the situation when I return from the South of France in late September. Another cup of tea?"'

'Miller & Co excused themselves, appalled that they'd been so greedy. For someone whose only contribution had been to suggest after the dress rehearsal that Bennett's services be dispensed with, Albery had done well.'

'Bennett was my favourite,' said Miranda. 'After the show he used to walk me home, pushing his bicycle, even though he lived on the other side of London. He'd say goodnight and then he'd pedal off in the opposite direction.'

What a sweet man he must have been, no doubt still is. The other day I knocked him off his bicycle in Shaftesbury Avenue and, before I could stop myself, I said how sorry I was that Godfrey Smith had recently bracketed him with Bernard Levin as a writer of English prose.

'It did seem to suggest that English might not be my first language,' said Bennett.

Actually I don't know what he said. He looked quite startled, having no idea who I was, I think, but he was courtesy itself. He said I must see him in his play at the Queens, but perhaps he says this to any punter who knocks him off his bicycle.

When I left Miranda after lunch she asked me, should I ever see me, to give me her love, and had I been me I might have cried, but since I was Lord Dynevor I couldn't. Instead I went home and passed clean out.

Perhaps I can persuade Lord Dynevor to do next week as me. Then he'll have to sit still for Dustin Hoffman in *The Merchant of Venice*, dining thereafter with my new friend Al, the film producer, on his night out from the lunatic asylum. I hope they find a restaurant which plays decent pop music as loudly as you like.

Fashion Dancing in Amsterdam

The lights were burning late into the night at Amsterdam's police headquarters last week – a result of the different approaches to research adopted by Mark Chapman, Jeremy Lovering and myself during a four-day reconnaissance of the European Community for our television series *Henry Root Into Europe*.

Lovering, the brains of the party, kept an open mind and carried a note book; I displayed British common sense, criticizing the Dutch over their obstinately illiberal policies on hard drugs; and Chapman bought some matching separates, put on two-and-a-half stone and got himself arrested.

In Brussels, where we pitched up first, Lovering and I were quite magnificent, introducing ourselves into official buildings, diving up and down corridors, poking and probing, and occasionally going out of bounds and being fielded by New Europeans – thin young men with enormous brains, girls with languages.

On Tuesday morning Lovering and I met William Martin who is in charge of Culture and Communications, and a delightful member of the European Parliament named Anthony Simpson (Northamptonshire, Conservative), while Chapman had a crab mousse wrapped in a green jacket, followed by medallion of pork with apple and raisin stuffing, served with a paprika-vodka sauce ('By no means disagreeable').

In the afternoon Lovering and I quizzed an even more delightful MEP called David Martin (Lothians, Labour), after which we took cocktails with Sir Leon Brittan, while Chapman settled for a crisp frissé lettuce topped with Italian cheese and croutons, served with a warm French dressing followed by fillet of beef served with a Stilton-port sauce and oregano-flavoured mushrooms ('A trifle bland').

Not that it was all work and no play for Lovering and me – rather the opposite, in fact. Before departure we had been a little worried that Chapman, who was carrying the money, might adopt a stuffbag attitude to after-hours research. Indeed, Lovering, who must be twenty-four or so, but is as much fun for all that as a man of fifty took me aside and said: 'A word in your ear, Button. How, after dark, do we shake off young Chapman?'

In the event we had no problem. At 10 p.m. precisely, Chapman would put himself to bed with a salad on his face, allowing Lovering and me to rendezvous with our pals, the New Europeans, who taught us, among other things, fashion dancing, which you master by inserting a pencil in your buttocks and drawing figures-of-eight on a convenient wall.

Over breakfast on our first morning in Amsterdam we reported this new skill to Chapman who was arrested later in the day for covering his bedroom walls with what were taken to be pornographic sketches. Invited to hop down to police head-quarters to bail him out, I took the opportunity to question the Commander of Police, Central Criminal Investigation Depart-ment, on the Dutch attitude to drugs and, more importantly, to bring him up to date with the latest thinking in the UK.

The Commander, a charming young man named Bob Visser, was justifiably proud of the fact that, by legalizing cannabis and unloading on dealers in hard drugs rather than on their cus-tomer, the Dutch – as would have been predicted by anyone with two brain cells to rub together – now have addiction figures which should be the envy of their EC partners. Nevertheless, I felt I had to mark his card on a couple of points.

'What about the crack problem?' I said.

'There isn't a crack problem in Amsterdam,' he said.

'Yes there is,' I said. 'You can't get it.'

He looked quite startled. 'Are you an addict?'

Why do people – even those as intelligent as this policeman – assume that if you take drugs you must be an addict? Drug users are much less likely than drinkers to abuse the intoxicant of their choice – a consequence, no doubt, of the fact that people who take drugs are nicer and more sensible than people who drink.

I told the Commander this and then explained that in the absence of a government-controlled supply of hard drugs, it was in the interests of criminals to peddle the stuff cut with heaven knows what dangerous rubbish. He might not have a crack problem now, I said, but he soon would have unless hard drugs were legalized.

The Commander looked thunderstruck. 'Is this the policy of the British Government?' he said.

'More or less,' I said.

'Excuse me,' he said, and then made ten phone calls simultaneously, alerting his men, I imagine, to the crack pandemic which was shortly to engulf them and advising politicians on the urgent need to change course and follow the liberal, British model. I left him to it, and I left Mark Chapman to it also, since he was too fat to get through the door of his cell where he still may be.

Minford Fails To Do His Stuff

It is disappointing to be out of step with the *Independent*, but I no longer agree with its recent editorial which argued for the legalization of hard drugs. My change of heart follows the reaction to last week's column in which, you may remember, I described my attempts to persuade Amsterdam's police chief of the urgent need to lift prohibition, pointing out that this was the policy of the British Government.

In making this claim I was, I now discover, overtaking events, as it were. I had, frankly, been misled by Dr John Marks, consultant psychiatrist to the Mersey Health Authority, with whom I had just had a most interesting conversation. Dr Marks, who, unusually in this debate, bases his arguments for legalization on clear evidence that such a policy works (not that this is any excuse) has, by the controlled prescribing of heroin and cocaine at two Merseyside clinics, reduced drug taking and acquisitive crime in the area and brought about an improvement in addicts' health. Even Mrs Thatcher, Dr Marks told me, might be impressed by this model. And pigs might fly, I said – somewhat coarsely, I am afraid, my only excuse being that I was quoting from the *Guardian*.

'And so they might,' said Dr Marks. 'My colleague, Richard Stevenson, works closely with Patrick Minford, Professor of Economics at Liverpool University and an adviser to Mrs Thatcher. I asked Stevenson how long it would take him to persuade Minford of the need to legalize. "About fifteen minutes," he said. The next time I saw him I asked him how he had done. "It took ten minutes." Stevenson then asked Minford how long it would take him to persuade Mrs Thatcher. "Mrs

16

Thatcher is very intelligent," Minford said, "About five minutes, I imagine."'

I went to Amsterdam assuming, wrongly, that Minford had done his stuff and that the Government's policy had changed. That is why I told the police chief that hard drugs had been legalized in Britain and why I wrote the piece I did. Imagine my surprise when I discovered that Mrs Thatcher had done nothing in my absence and my even greater surprise when I was accused by my best friend, Little Jo, of encouraging people to try crack. Her contempt for what I had written made me think more carefully about drugs.

I wrote out of impatience, I think, with the Government-inspired hysteria surrounding crack. Describing the high you get from it, an American busybody recently said: 'Imagine an orgasm. Multiply that by ten and you're there.' Life is short and anyone refusing the stuff after this publicity would be an odd fish indeed – but the plug, like most PR, is not true. Such an endorsement could only come from someone who had never had an orgasm or who had never had crack, possibly both.

It is pleasant, however, if somewhat unsocial – not solipsistic – in its operation, making you want to behave yourself indoors with compatible intimates rather than pick a fight in a pub with a stranger who has vomited on your shoes. Its most startling effect is to make you nicer than you are, so anyone who is already happy, hard-working and unselfish is unlikely to be altered much. Nor is it instantly, or even in the long run, particularly addictive. I have smoked it at irregular intervals for several years with a variety of people, only one of whom has experienced any difficulties. You *choose* to become hooked on cocaine which, unlike alcohol or heroin, is not a physically addictive drug, and I rather resent plumfaced lunchtime types suggesting that, because of some psychological dysfunction, I cannot control my liking for it as efficiently as they can control their preference for a £250 bottle of wine.

In sum, I agreed with the *Independent* that associated problems were caused not by the drug itself but by the criminal context in which it has to be acquired and taken. Now I have been per-suaded to a different view by Ronald Siegel's *Intoxication* (Simon & Schuster, £15.95). Professor Siegel, who believes that the desire for intoxication is a fourth drive – as unstoppable as hunger, thirst and sex – but is against legalization (on the grounds that this would lead to a small, but undesirable, increase in the number of addicts), recently discovered that for over two years hundreds of little old ladies with arthritis had been treated in a California hospital with Esterene – a trade name for crack – without a single case of abuse.

If crack could be used without abuse, Siegel realized, then the difference between use and abuse was one of dose. 'Calvinistic pharmacology,' he writes, 'has prevented us from seeing pleasurable changes in the body or mind as fulfilling health needs. It is time we recognize intoxicants as medicines and intoxications as treatments for the human condition.' Instead of fighting unwinnable wars, he concludes, governments should develop intoxicants as safe and unabusable as the foods we eat. That is never likely to happen, of course, so I will continue to pay over the odds for my intoxicant, while other inadequates can acquire warm gin in a theatre bar for next to nothing.

Skiing in Florida with Daddy

My best friend, Little Jo, has been trying to convince me that there is no snow in Florida at this time of year, but I know better because my literary agent, Alison, is out there skiing at the moment with her father. Why Little Jo should try to unsettle me like this I cannot imagine. I trust Alison completely – which is something of a one-way arrangement, as it happens, bearing in mind that I have not told her yet that she is no longer my sole representative.

For some weeks now I have had two literary agents: Alison, who is perfect in every respect, and Cat Ledger, who, since she is in New York at the moment, won't mind my saying in her absence that she is one of the rudest, most difficult women I have ever met. Since, before Alison, it had been my practice to have at least four agents at any one time – two on the field, as it were, and two more limbering up on the touchline to make the others nervous – I could see nothing wrong with this arrangement but just before flying off to New York, Cat Ledger told me that

18

readers of this column were confusing her with Alison – drawing wrong conclusions about the nature of our relationship – and that she would be obliged if I would make it clear who was exactly who. She had her reputation to think of, she said. *Her* reputation indeed! What about mine?

Problems started with Alison one evening several weeks ago when we were watching *Chariots of Fire* on television. Suddenly I realized what was wrong with the British film industry; it was a case, obviously, of too much money chasing too little talent and I said as much to Alison.

'Selling stuff to these bozos must be like shooting fish in a barrel,' I said. 'Let's get some films set up.'

'Right,' said Alison. 'Just as long as you don't expect me to do anything. It's always a mistake, in my experience, to mix business with business. I need some new ski boots, by the way.'

That seemed fair, so I ran around for a few days selling a book here and another there, later reporting to Alison how well I had done. We were in Jasper Conran's at the time, inspecting his new range of ski equipment, which was a bit of a waste of time, actually, because he didn't have a range of ski equipment, but Alison didn't seem too surprised, making do instead with a selection of summer after-dark ensembles and après-beach access-ories. I told her that I had sold several of my books to odd young men in boastfully wide suits and *en brosse* haircuts – or the same book several times, I could not remember which – and that I now needed her to unscramble the confusion.

'I can't be bothered with that at the moment,' she said. 'Per-haps I'll have time to look into it after I get back from my skiing holiday in Florida with Daddy.'

I decided on the spot to engage another agent – if only temporarily – and shortly after this I happened to bump into my old friend, Cat Ledger, who has always seemed to me to have all the qualities of a good representative, being as tough as boots, able to divide $171\frac{1}{3}$ by $13\frac{3}{4}$ in seconds in her head and possess-ing a fine contempt for the small proportion of my stuff which she has had the courtesy to read. I instructed her to go to work on my behalf and I have to say that, within days of her taking over, Wardour Street and its environs were littered with film producers who looked as terminally shaken up as Icky Woods – the Cincinatti Bengals' over-confident running-back – did after

Ronnie Lott, the finest free-safety in the NFL, unloaded on him at the start of Super Bowl XXIII.

Plus, and less happily, my ex-best friend, Justin Judd – the producer of my television series *Henry Root Into Europe* – who thought he had a deal with me but discovered in no time that he hadn't, is now mumbling distractedly to himself, walking into walls and sitting in the office with a kettle on his head, whereas he was once 6ft 4ins with the broad back and steady tread of a man who has estates in Scotland.

Before she flew to New York this week I took Ledger out to lunch to celebrate. 'Well done,' I said.

'Thank you,' she said. 'I wish to lodge a serious complaint, however. The small minority of my clients who glance at your column have been asking me whether I'm having some sort of affair with you.'

'Don't worry,' I said. 'I'm sure I can live that down.'

'You don't understand,' she said. 'They have come to the conclusion that I must be Alison.'

I was flabbergasted. 'How could that happen?' I said. 'As I've made clear week after week, Alison is quite unnaturally perfect – as beautiful, as graceful and uncaring as an oriental cat – whereas you are one of the rudest, most unpleasant women I've ever met. You want me to say this in my column?'

'I'd be obliged,' she said.

So there you are. With Alison and Ledger both out of the country at the same time, this seemed the moment to clear up the confusion once and for all.

Alison, My Beloved, and Page Three Tracey

My literary agent, Alison, has been commissioned for a six-figure sum to write a book called *Journo*, the – to my mind – rather patronising account of how a pretty young Page Three model becomes obsessed with a comic old party in a corduroy suit, a vaguely literary chap who volunteers opinions in a lower-middlebrow paper. Before telling me this, Alison – sweetly tanned and looking as pleased as Punch after her skiing holiday in Florida – was decent enough to ask me if anything of interest had happened in her absence.

I did have one piece of good news in fact, but I judged it best not to pass it on. The week before Paul Sidey, the most hard-headed of Random Century's many accomplished young editors, had suggested over a fish lunch that I write a book about her.

'You seem to have made a hash of things,' he'd said. 'All your stuff taken away by the repossession men, your life at risk from Ken Australian Horse Player. What a mess. How serious, by the way, is the threat from Ken?'

'Very serious.'

'Good. You won't mind my saying that your stock would go up – we're talking about point-of-sale – if you were a dead duck when the book came out. I suggest you write about addiction. Runs in the family, does it? Perhaps that's neither here nor there. I'm referring to your pitiful compulsion not to know what will happen next, your obsession with literary agents who are utterly careless and elusive. From Sunningdale to this. Oh dear, oh dear. I could offer you as much as £1000. Are you on?'

I'd said I was. The charge of addiction was obviously trite and amateurish, but the £1000 would come in handy, since Alison's holiday with her father would almost certainly turn out to have cost more than I'd been expecting. I was obliged, it seemed to me, to tell her that I had, in her absence, replaced her as my literary agent – if only temporarily – with Cat Ledger. On the other hand I decided that I must on no account, tell her about the book. She doesn't read my stuff but might suspect that what I'd write about her would be ignorant and patronising.

'I've been commissioned to write a book about you,' I said.

'Never mind that,' said Alison. 'Listen. I've got a new literary agent, Pat Kavanagh. She's brilliant. She's got me a small fortune to write a book called *Journo*. It's about this model called Tracey, right? She's pretty and clever, and has never been off the rails, but then she throws it all away on this old twit. He's a writer, okay? "The Man Who Says What Others Scarcely Dare to Think".'

'What does he write about?'

'Soda-water syphons.'

'Good heavens.'

'Exactly.'

'Why?'

'You can't get them. He's concerned too about the disappearing small shopkeeper. And telephone kiosks.'

'They're disappearing too?'

'No. But they aren't red any more.'

'Get away.'

'No, really. And he corrects her grammar and makes jokes about polytechnic teachers called Len Trot.'

'A bit right wing, is he?'

'Yorkshire left of centre, in fact. But he admits to a sneaking regard for Norman Tebbit.'

'That's good.'

'And guess what? He takes her into pubs!'

'You're exaggerating.'

'He *does*!' Alison was shaking with laughter, I don't know why. 'What's that book?'

'What book?'

'That new book. You know.'

'*Titmuss Postponed*?'

'Well done. What do you think he says about it?'

'Highly entertaining?'

'"It commits the cardinal sin these days of being hugely readable".'

'That is audacious.'

'Exactly. She becomes obsessed with his mind, do you see?'

'It isn't sexual, then?'

'It is for her, even though he calls it "horizontal jogging"! It's a matter of self-ignition. She can climax on his unpredictable opinions. Her friends – Sharon and Kevin and so forth – snigger behind his back and write down what he says in notebooks but she's never heard such stuff expressed in all seriousness in public. He is displeased, for instance, by motorway food. And what do you suppose is his contribution to a discussion on *The Satanic Verses*?'

'"I couldn't put it down, but I'm against free speech"?'

'Don't be silly,' said Alison.

It is she and her literary adviser, Pat Kavanagh, who are being silly, if you ask me. Just because her narrator, Tracey, is young and pretty and clever, that doesn't give her the right to patronise silly old sods like 'The Man Who Says What Others Scarcely Dare to Think' for being old and ridiculous and out of it.

My own book for Random Century will be altogether more serious, and next week I will set off on the long journey into my past – all the way to Sunningdale, to be precise.

Tour de Farce

I'm bucketing around France in the back of a Volvo at the moment researching my TV series, *Henry Root Into Europe*. For the next four weeks I'll be living out of a suitcase – more accurately, out of a carrier bag, having discovered when I came to pack that I didn't have a suitcase. It's just as well I'm travelling light since my three partners on the jaunt (Mark Chapman, Justin Judd and Jeremy Lovering) are carting along enough in the way of clothes, haberdashery and toiletries to equip a party of German call-girls visiting the Cannes Film Festival.

You can't blame them, I suppose since it is the misfortune of young people these days not to have done National Service. Soon after I joined the Navy I was surprised to discover that the captain and officers of my submarine all suffered from sea sickness. Within minutes of our setting off on an important Nato exercise, they turned pea-green and announced that they didn't want to know, leaving me no alternative but to drive the thing from Portsmouth to Gibraltar where I further distinguished myself by parking it under the enemy flagship – the Royal Yacht, as it happened – and waiting until the starting gun went off, where upon I lobbed a grenade on to the bridge, followed by a 'Yah boo, you're dead' signal. There was a bit of a rumpus – a leader in *The Times*, indignant letters from old salts, etc – and our captain, who couldn't admit that he'd been in his bunk since leaving Portsmouth, was severely reprimand. That's as may be; my point is that ferrying a Volvo and three tarts across Europe is a doddle by comparison.

I'd been in two minds, I must admit, as to whether to come along (the prospect of all the filthy meals ahead had caused me to inflate like the Michelin man on the front of that silly guide), but at the last minute I decided to pitch up with a month's supply of Bisodol, and it's just as well I did. Without me the enterprise would have been up the creek, since the three girls – Judd, Lovering and Chapman – may look very nice but in an emergency they don't stack up.

Judd, the producer, hasn't recovered from the duffing up he suffered at the hands of my temporary literary agent, Cat Ledger, and is clearly a broken man. A master hitherto of logistics and sophisticated budgeting, he once took a thousand or so Equity members into the jungle without losing more than an acceptable percentage, but he now sits in the back of the Volvo in a hat, singing country-and-western songs. Chapman, frankly, is an artist, seeing life through an imaginary viewfinder (when he isn't snout down in the Michelin guide, that is), while Lovering, our researcher, is an intellectual and sulking anyway – the latter condition caused by my having remarked before departure that he was looking rather plain. He'd had his head styled locally – always a mistake – swopping a helicopter landing-pad effect for a pert *en brosse* which does very little for him.

Happily, all three can recognize a naval man when they see one and they saw one when the bottom fell out of the Volvo three miles into France. Judd sat in the road whimpering, Chapman, head buried in the Michelin, didn't know we'd stopped, and Lovering said he was a post-feminist and didn't want to spoil his nails. No problem. I took over, faxing my people here and there, and conjuring up spare parts – enabling us to reach Paris in time to rendezvous with the captain of police at the Fifth Precinct who had agreed to let us accompany his men on a night patrol as part of our research.

We *would* have been in time, that is, if Lovering hadn't argued at the last minute that he didn't have anything to wear for such an outing and that he wished anyway to do his ironing. Then Chapman said he wasn't going to hurry his dinner to accommodate a captain of police, with the result that by the time we reached the station enough crime had piled up on the streets of Paris to keep us and the French Old Bill busy for the rest of the evening.

And a very interesting evening it was, in the course of which I discovered that French criminals and the general public also defer to a naval man when one such moves among them. I don't want

24

to make too much of this. Obviously, if several Gauloise-smoking French policemen came pelting up your front stairs, followed at a sensible distance by a smart old party in a suit, you'd take the smart old party to be in charge.

I dispensed justice even-handedly, I think, which is more than can be said for Chapman, who seemed – either from an excess of enthusiasm for law and order or because his dinner hadn't settled – to be in favour of batoning everything that moved.

When we got back to the hotel I was keen to discuss this worrying phenomenon with Lovering, who would be in his room, I assumed, sewing roses on to his disco slippers or whatever it is that, post-feminists do. Instead I found him in the TV lounge, eyes out like organ stops, watching *Tutti Frutti* in which Italian housewives take their clothes off and then perform Continental evolutions. What do you make of that? So much for post-feminism, I say.

The Falcon has Landed

If this space is blank today, I'll be upside down in the Tiber and you'll never know it's a mistake to see *A Chorus Line* in Italian underwear. The in-depth reconnaissance of the Continent for my television series, *Henry Root Into Europe*, continues at a furious pace and for the three girls – Mark Chapman, Jeremy Lovering and Justin Judd – laundry has become the issue. I'm filing this – courtesy of the Mafia, I rather think – from Palermo airport where, for the last twenty-four hours, Chapman and I, watched over by a platoon of extravagantly armed *carabinieri*, have been kicking our heels in a holding area for problematic visitors, while our linen and half hose are in Milan with Judd and Lovering.

As a naval man, accustomed to wearing the same clothes at ninety feet for weeks on end, I don't give two hoots, of course, but Chapman, who for the first time in his life has now worn the same shirt on consecutive days, is becoming more morose by the minute.

On Monday, we were living comfortably in Rome when word came through that Giovanni Falcone – Palermo's dramatically courageous investigating magistrate who has vowed to crush the Mafia – had agreed to see us at one of his secret hideaways. Judd and Lovering remembered urgent other business in Milan, but Chapman and I – taking with us nothing but the clothes we stood up in – flew to Palermo where, as I say, we've been held in a small room for the last twenty-four hours, while the *carabinieri* try to track Falcone down.

This is quite a problem. Falcone trusts no one but himself, changes his circumstances as frequently as Chapman changes his shirts, never informs others of his new whereabouts until he reaches them and, if possible, omits to do so even then. Nor, bearing in mind the fate of many of his predecessors in the job, can you blame him for taking these precautions. A current Calabrian joke, in extremely bad taste it seems to me (and one which I now made the mistake of passing on to Chapman), suggests that Falcone's life expectancy is so short that if he ordered a three-minute egg he'd be asked to pay in advance.

Chapman became so agitated when I told him this that, as the senior officer present, so to speak, I tried to cheer him up by pointing out that, as far as our armed escort was concerned, the odds were in our favour.

'There is no reason to be apprehensive,' I said. 'If current calculations are correct we can assume that a small majority of these chaps are working for Falcone rather than for the Mafia.'

'I'm not apprehensive,' said Chapman.

'Why, then, have you been wearing a false nose ever since we left Rome?'

'I'm not wearing a false nose,' he said.

I took a closer look. 'Nor you are. I'm so sorry.'

'In fact,' he said, 'I'm worried about my underwear which I've had on now since yesterday.'

I was shocked, frankly. Here we were, hours merely, days at most, away from a major scoop and all Chapman could think about was his laundry. I gave him a short blast about shipping it green and life at ninety feet, and then suggested that the *carabinieri* might be persuaded to buy him some knickers at a nearby menswear shop.

'I wouldn't risk that,' said Chapman. 'Did you see *A Chorus Line* by any chance?'

'Certainly not,' I said.

'If I tell you something in the strictest confidence, will you promise to keep it to yourself?'

'Of course.'

'Some years ago,' he said, 'I bought some underwear when shooting a film in Italy. As you may know, Italian knickers wouldn't cover a postage stamp. For some reason I took a pair back to London and put them on one night to impress a girl I'd met in Italy. She wanted to see *A Chorus Line*. It's always a mistake to see a musical, of course, even more so if you're in Italian underwear. As soon I sat down, I felt as if my balls had been caught in a badger trap. By the time the overture had finished I was squinting with pain. Never mind, I thought, I'll go to the Gents in the interval and take them off. Then I looked at the programme. There wasn't an interval, if you please.'

'Always a gloomy discovery at a musical.'

'Precisely. I then tried to calculate how long the thing would last. An old tart stepped forward and told her story. That's it, I thought. Then I noticed that there were four old tarts on stage and that each of them was going to have her say. It was the worst moment of my life. When the show ended I ran up an alley and took my knickers off. You mustn't put this in your column. Jane, my beloved, knows nothing of it and wouldn't understand.'

'Don't worry,' I said, 'I'll say it happened to Justin Judd.'

'That's all right then,' said Chapman.

At this moment we got a message that Falcone was back in Rome and would be happy to see us there. I had just time, before catching a plane, to ask one of the *carabinieri* to fax this to London for me, so if it doesn't appear we'll know he was working on the wrong side – also why Chapman and I are upside down in the Tiber. That, at least, will solve the laundry problem.

Sordid Old Men and Acquisitive Tarts

For a naval man, shepherding the three girls round Europe, amusing them with my salty anecdotes, squaring my shoulders when the chips are down, has been a piece of cake, in fact, so I have had time on my hands to brood over my upcoming book about addiction, *From Sunningdale to This*.

I now see that I blew my bags too soon on this one when, a week or two ago, I boasted here that I personally – precisely because I lacked an artistic temperament, imperfectly expressed or otherwise – would never abuse the drug of my choice.

Since I urgently need a fix, such a temperament is not, clearly, a necessary condition of addiction. After a mere three weeks away, my withdrawal symptoms are appalling. More interesting, I think, than the obvious ones – cold sweats, sleeplessness, loss of concentration – is an awesome punctuality, which is in sharp contrast to the three girls' dotty inability to know what time, or even what day, it is and is a function not, as I at first imagined, of my naval background but of a crushing boredom with the present, an addict's agitated need to press on to the next stage, whatever horrors may there unfold.

In sum, I miss my literary agent, Alison, dream continuously of her youthful, absent-minded candour, her thrilling unconcern, yearn for her cool indifference to the small thoughtful tokens I've collected for her on my travels – a matchbox from Baden-Baden, a sugar lump from Florence. I must persuade the girls that we need a break, steer them towards Ibiza where I'll ditch them, jet my baby in, wear trousers and walk from the waist, spread her on a beach and eye her proudly from a distance, engage my pal Tanit the Island God – the heavy centre of Ibiza's in-crowd, a stone-nude negro in a bejewelled *cache-sexe* – in casual conversation.

'Hi man, what's happening? Cool running hey hey hey.'

Driving this week from Milan to Barcelona, and with this scenario in mind, I suggested this change in our arrangements to the three girls. 'Enough's enough,' I said. 'We need a break. Let's go to Ibiza for a week.'

Judd, our producer, whimpered and Chapman said: *'Ibiza?* The food there must be disgusting.'

'Nonsense,' I said. 'It's a paradise on earth.' Then I asked Lovering, our travelling post-feminist and intellectual, to read out the entry on it from *The Rough Guide to Europe*.

'Okay,' he said. 'Right. Here it is. Inhabited by dirty old codgers and acquisitive little tarts . . .'

'Do what?'

'Sorry,' said Lovering. 'I skipped a bit. The historical perspective. The enduring fascination of Ibiza consists in its unique evolution. It was first settled by three tribes who arrived from different parts of the world. From the north came the cool lords of commerce, from the south the artists, from the east the thinkers. For many years, the three tribes lived in perfect harmony, resolving their differences in a sane and intelligent manner. Then one day a fat man in a tub was washed ashore. Claiming to be an ancient mariner of noble seafaring stock, it soon became apparent that he had arrived from a land in the west dedicated to decadence.'

'Steady on,' said Chapman.

'There's more,' said Lovering. 'Accustomed to living off seaweed and barnacles, he arrived on the beach belching and boasting of maritime adventures that had never happened. Amazingly, he wormed his way into the inhabitants' confidence, spreading his foul gospel of greed and debauchery.

'Pulling evil-smelling substances from his pocket, he stuffed them into a pipe, which he passed around among the innocent settlers. In a gesture of genuine philistinism, he lit the pipe with their works of art. Turning their backs in disgust, the three tribes abandoned their sullied paradise to the debauched, self-advertising sea captain, who, master now of the land he had polluted, dedicated himself to hedonism.'

'What of the present?' said Chapman. 'What of his descendants? What does it say of them?'

'The majority,' said Lovering, 'are slaves to drugs and to their fatuous vanity. Few can work but one or two are fortunate enough to gain occasional employment as Saturday journalists, inflating their egos in a flurry of exhibitionism, filling their columns with gauche references to honourable people glimpsed from a distance.

'When not praising themselves, they use their columns to damage their friends. Artists who allow themselves the luxury of an occasional claret are abused as obsessive foodies; businessmen with ice-pick brains are humiliated into crooning sulkers; and the friend who is lucky enough to be a true thinker is dumped on the rotting pile as a post-feminist, a term which the Saturday show-off hasn't even bothered to understand. Misquoting Larkin, plagiarising Amis, he pirouettes ludicrously, a broken old man, a . . .'

'That's enough,' said Chapman kindly.

'Water off a duck's back,' I said. 'Are we going to Ibiza or what?'

A Loose Cannon in Barcelona

There's a boll weevil in the ship's biscuits, and I don't mean Lovering. I won't name names, but Justin Judd will know who I'm talking about.

Last week, you may remember, I and the three girls – Chapman, Lovering and Judd – were cruising in good order between Milan and Barcelona when Lovering ran amok in my column, calling me a sordid old codger and suggesting that I use this space simply to betray my friends.

I hadn't spotted Lovering as a loose cannon, I must admit, and for the rest of the journey I tried to work out how best to secure the ship against further subversion.

By the time we reached Barcelona my plans were laid. In order to protect the enterprise it would be necessary, I realized, to throw the trio into a turmoil of confused loyalties, make each in turn believe I was his special pal, team up temporarily with one and set the isolated pair at one another's throats.

And here I had a problem. Judd, on the face of it, seemed a natural ally, if only for reasons of class (I'm not saying the other two are common – merely that, when the torpedoes are running, background counts) but Judd hadn't recovered yet from the duffing up he'd received from my temporary literary, Cat Ledger.

Or had he? Driving through Perpignan, he'd suddenly woken from a deep sleep, stared at me penetratingly and said: 'Sheridan Morley? Stacks up for you, does he, Commander?'

Then he'd gone to sleep again. An hour later he'd woken just as suddenly, fixed me with an eagle eye and said: 'Until the age of twenty-six I'd never eaten lamb which hadn't been raised on my own estates. What do you say to that?'

Bearing in mind the state he'd been in during the first three weeks of the recce, I took these disconnected observations as an indication that his brain was beginning to function normally again, indeed, that he was ready to play his part in my scheme to deharmonize the group – which was, more or less, to involve them in a moral obstacle race, confident, because of conflicting attitudes previously in evidence, that none could win without tripping up the others. (Lovering and I, for instance, are keenly censorious when it comes to sex, more liberal in other areas. With Chapman it's vice versa. Obliged to meet a mad old tart in Italy who was standing for parliament on a 'people should be allowed to do it in the streets' platform, Chapman had been quite impressed, Lovering and I greatly shocked. 'What you need, madam, is a cold shower,' I'd said – advice I'd already offered to the cast of a dirty show in Hamburg which Lovering and I had left after a few minutes, judging it to be a blasphemy against everything we held sacred and admitting that, for the first time, we now knew how it felt to have one's religion mocked. Chapman had called us a couple of prigs and might still be there had we not dragged him out.)

Be that as it may, I now confronted Chapman first with my moral problem.

'A word in your ear,' I said. 'I cashed a travellers' cheque at the Banco Bilbao this morning and they overpaid me by £500. What do you think I should do?'

'Take it back,' said Chapman.

'But there's no victim, as far as I can see.'

'Nonsense,' said Chapman. 'The shortfall will be discovered and the cashier, who may well be nursing his crippled mother, will be fired.'

I had to admit the force of this argument. 'Stuff him,' I said.

Next I put my problem to Lovering who side-stepped it rather neatly by saying that he couldn't get involved in a moral dilemma which wasn't his.

Finally, I approached Justin Judd, more confident that he would react like an English gentleman.

'Not a word to the others,' I said, 'but I've just had a windfall of £500 from the Banco Bilbao. What do you think I ought to do?'

'Share it with me,' said Judd without hesitation, 'and I won't tell Chapman and Lovering.'

'Good man,' I said. 'Let's go further. Let's fire Chapman and produce the series ourselves. We're sitting on a gold-mine.'

'I'm with you all the way,' said Judd. Imagine my surprise when, later that night, I came across Judd and Chapman in a bar, laughing fit to bust.

'What's so funny?' I asked.

'You,' said Judd. 'And your temporary literary agent, Cat Ledger. I was merely feigning dim-wittedness to lull you into a false sense of security. We've done you up like a kipper. We even have the book rights in the series.'

'May I have them back?'

'Only if you promise not to make any more jokes about us in your column.'

'All right,' I said.

Next week we visit a farm in Jerez where they breed fighting bulls.

As you may know, bulls offer no threat when in the company of oxen – the post-feminists, as it were, of the cattle world.

I reckon I'll be quite safe if I stick close to the three girls whom the bulls will recognise as honorary oxen, so to speak.

Thin English Legs and a Ginger Beard

We are on the last lap of the recce now – a huge loop round Spain, a night in France with my friend Baron Rothschild, then home – and the fact that I'm no longer in the Volvo with the three girls (Chapman, Lovering and Judd) but in a Ford Fiesta with a new face on the team (Garry Marvin, Wykeham Professor of Bulls at the University of East Anglia) is no indication that morale has broken down completely.

Far from it. The time has come, indeed, to admit that what I've said here previously about the girls has been somewhat fanciful, quite untrue, in fact. They're not really girls, at all, but three of the most straight-up chaps a man could go on manoeuvres with, and nothing better illustrates what all-round good eggs they are, I think, than the fact that, increasingly in the last few days, they've disappeared for hours on end to buy small thoughtful presents for those they left at home.

All except Chapman, that is. He's been buying large thoughtful presents and pitched up today with several parcels, boastfully wrapped.

'What have you got there?' I asked.

'A bottle of scent, an Armani blouse, a handbag from Florence and some rather nice earrings.'

'Nothing for Jane, your beloved, then?'

'It's enough for her,' he said, 'that I return home looking my very best.'

That's the sort of chap he is, and I decided to complete the recce with Professor Marvin in the Fiesta simply because I judged that only I, of the original team, was socially adroit enough to put the professor – roped in to advise us on the finer points of Spain's cultural heritage – fully at his ease.

I should point out too, perhaps, that I didn't know he was a professor when I made my decision, but had him down as one of those odd young men from Essex who suddenly go mad and decide to become Spaniards, without having the legs for it, or the upper arms either, come to that, but set off none the less to be chased by bulls up back streets and to march, with disgusting little girls in make-up, to slack drums at superstitious festivals – returning to Essex after three weeks to have their sinuses drained on the NHS. As we drove out of Barcelona on the long journey to Granada and Seville, I smiled encouragingly and asked him how long he'd been a researcher in Spain.

'I'm not a researcher and I don't live in Spain,' he said.

'Really? What *do* you do?'

'I'm an academic. Philosophy, originally, then anthropology. My PhD thesis was called *La Corrida des Toros: An Anthropological Study of Animal and Human Nature.*'

My spirits rose. To have captive for several hundred miles an expert on the *corrida*, with a smattering of philosophy, was a dream come true.

'Why did you give up philosophy?' I asked.

'Too stupid,' he said. 'I'm a second-class anthropologist, too. I can't master the jargon. I look at what I've written with disgust.

33

"A child of six could understand this," I think. "Great heavens, *I* can understand it! It can't be any good.'"

I became more and more excited. I too like jargon, prefer to have the wool pulled over my eyes, don't think I'm getting my money's worth unless being bamboozled by abstractions from abroad.

'My feelings precisely,' I said.

'You've read my work?'

'No no. I was referring to my own stuff actually.'

'Ah yes,' the professor said. 'That's very poor. Like a man grinning half-wittedly with a hatchet in his head. Take this week's column: the silly joke about Chapman, and calling me a Professor of Bulls. Quite pointless. A journalist should impart information. From you we learn nothing.'

'I don't know anything,' I said. 'Except what time it is. I always know that. It's a function of my addiction. Even when I'm enjoying myself I like to know what time it is. Ah, six o'clock, I think. That's good. Not much more of this. While you've been burbling on I've worked out that I shall see my literary agent, Alison, in exactly five days, six hours, thirty-three minutes and ten seconds.'

'You don't mind my criticism, then?'

'Not in the least,' I said. 'It's praise I can't handle. I feel ashamed and agitated, as if I'd squeezed cash out of an over-drawn account. I once received a thundering compliment in public from a respected novelist. I've avoided him ever since.'

'That's strange,' the professor said. 'I once had a similar experience. I was invited to deliver a paper at a seminar on the *corrida* at Barcelona University. I was immensely nervous, hardly heard the other papers – delivered by every expert in the country – scrambled through mine somehow and then sat down. When it was time for comments from the floor, Professor Manuel Santez, Spain's leading authority on the *corrida*, stood up and said: "Only one person here tonight has talked any sense. And it wasn't that prat of an Englishman with thin legs and a ginger beard."'

My Pal the Count

I don't want everyone to know (I don't want anyone to know, in fact) but I got back from the recce a week ago and I'm in a bit of a flap because my new best friend, Count Alvaro Domecq, is coming to stay. I met him on the last lap of the recce when the girls – Chapman, Lovering and Judd – and I visited him on his bull farm in Andalusia.

He's a very nice man but, like everyone who lives in the country, he was obviously bored to tears and touchingly keen that we shouldn't leave. I wasn't surprised; it must be a nightmare, stuck away in the middle of nowhere with scenery everywhere you look. Justin Judd was a little grudging ('Stuff this, I'd take Scotland anytime,' he said) but the rest of us – as any sensitive city dwellers would have done, I think – tried to cheer him up.

'Nice place you've got here!' I said, adding, for courtesy's sake I suppose, that if he ever felt like getting back into it all – discovering through the hurly-burly of the rat race who he really was and so forth – he must spend a weekend with me in London. I didn't expect him to take me up on the offer, of course, but today I received a card advising me that he'd be pitching up at my place on Friday morning.

This was a bit of a bombshell. Although I've been back for a week I still seem to be suffering from Volvo lag. I'm suspended between realities, physically here, I think, but not in any other sense. I don't know where I am. I'm neither here nor there, and certainly not ready yet to do the things I *do* want to do – see Terence Blacker, have lunch with Susan Carr, hang up on Pratley, that's about it – never mind the things I don't want to do, which is everything else (open the mail, answer the telephone, worry about Ben Elton, etc.).

On top of which I miss the girls most horribly. I still see them, of course, indeed I spend the day at Chapman's office working on the script, but it isn't the same. We still rehearse our little running jokes, tentatively try to play out the reassuring roles we picked for ourselves on tour, but they don't work as well as they did in some daft place such as Florence or Sienna.

Today, for instance, Justin Judd – my favourite, as it happens,

35

and the other two won't mind my saying this – poked his head round the office door and said:

'Joan Thirkettle? Stacks up for you, does she, Commander?'

It was a good try, but it wasn't the same; it didn't have the edge it would have done on the steps of the Alhambra. It was a courtesy, merely, a heartbreaking refusal to admit that everything was over – like talking about the cats or, less seriously, the children during a painful divorce. Equally, my ordering a sausage sandwich and a raspberry milkshake at the Rue St Jacques in Charlotte Street and then blowing cheap cigar smoke over Chapman's *foie gras de canards en chartreuse* is very funny, of course, but it doesn't undo him as effectively as when I did the same at the Tour D'Argent.

We were ships that pass in the night, the girls and I; they've gone back to their wives and so forth, and I've got to face the fact.

I've also got to face the fact that Count Alvaro is coming to stay on Friday. What on earth will he expect? Authoritarians with large, half-witted dogs who angrily summon you to Hampshire, or wherever, clearly want to administer the short, sharp shock of a weekend in the country; they want to punish you for not making the same mistake as they did thirty years ago. I used to fall for these invitations – indignantly delivered, as if it would be good for you to talk about trees for a couple of days, poke bonfires and sit at a stiff dinner party next to a JP's lady – but not any more. I used to hop into my car on Saturday morning, drive to Gloucestershire, get lost, seek directions from the village idiot, step in a puddle in my London pumps and finally arrive, stinking like a ditch, to find one's host and hostess getting drunk. They're all alcoholics in the country and who shall blame them?

'Ah, there you are,' they used to say. 'Make yourself at home.'

'Thank you very much,' one should have said. 'I'll do just that if I may; return immediately to London for a decent meal and a made-for TV movie.'

They should pay you, really, for visiting them – something I always had the courtesy to do when I had a place in Ibiza. Lonely as hell and needing company, I'd ring someone up in London and ask them if they'd like a week in the sun.

'How much?' they said.

'A thousand pounds,' I said, 'plus a run round the boutiques with my Access card.'

'Okay,' they said – and then we all knew where we stood.

On this analysis, Count Alvaro will expect to be thrown head first into the worst that London has to offer: Sunday lunch surrounded by psychopathic children, a drink in a Soho pub, a visit to a musical, warm gin in the interval, being stuck in the rain in Shaftesbury Avenue without a taxi home. I couldn't do this to him; I couldn't do it to myself, what's more. He'll have to take it as he finds it: the siege mentality, the thrill of being one step ahead of the repossession men, the subdued lights and seventies music – three rings on the doorbell means it's Winston with the gear at last, and thank God for that.

The trouble is, he'll enjoy himself so much he'll never leave.

It's Okay If the Curtains are Drawn

It was silly of me, I suppose, to write here last week that I was back at last from my lengthy tour of Europe but that I didn't want anyone to know. I'd quite forgotten, obviously, how many people read the *Independent*. Even if I had remembered this, however, it wouldn't have occurred to me, I must admit, that my temporary literary agent, Cat Ledger, might be among them.

Further, the knowledge that she was an *Independent* reader wouldn't in itself have struck me as a serious breach of security. In my experience, literary agents – even those who read their clients' stuff – want a quiet life and the last thing they are likely to do is pass on such expressions of interest in you or your work as are directed by mistake through them.

I assume, for instance, that all the agents I have been with in the last twenty years still think they represent me since I've not heard from one of them since the day they took me on. (My friend J.P. Donleavy argues, on the other hand, that the great thing about not having an agent is that you can be washed up for two years without knowing it – on the grounds, presumably, that the first person to tell you that you've had it is your agent. On this analysis, perhaps I'm not doing as badly as I thought.)

That's as may be, and Cat Ledger, I should have realized, hasn't yet got the hang of things at all, taking the job seriously and – providing you don't mind having a temporary literary agent who wishes to further your career – performing it quite brilliantly. The first indication I received that the jig was up vis-à-vis my whereabouts came when she rang me at Mark Chapman's office and gave me a rocket for not telling her promptly enough that I was back in the country.

The *Observer* – keen *Independent* readers, it seemed – had been on to her, she said, wanting to feature me in their excellent 'A Room of My Own' series in the colour supplement. Was I interested? Since my preference for living like a recluse – almost, indeed, as if I don't exist – never prevails against the natural desire to have my privacy invaded whenever possible, I agreed instantly and a date was made for a young reporter on the paper to visit me on Thursday.

I was quite looking forward to this, I must admit, since it's always nice to talk about oneself and I assumed that the *Observer*, unlike the *Sunday Times*, say, would be more interested in my views on this and that than in my circumstances. Not that, if it had occurred to me that their interest might be in how I lived, this would have bothered me. Since there is no reason to advertise how well one's doing, particularly when one's doing rather badly, my place isn't the Ritz but it's jolly nice and suits me excellently. I was in a good mood, therefore, when I opened my front door to a crisp young girl from the *Observer*.

'Good God,' she said, and her jaw actually dropped – not something I'd seen before.

'What's up?' I said. 'Mind the cat.'

'Do you *live* here?' she said, taking a step back – another thing I'd not seen before – 'It's a *tip*.'

I was quite surprised, hurt even. In fact, my wife and I did the place up a few years ago – or rather half did it up. We went a bit mad one day and decided to do away with the bottle-green curtains and carpet, replace them with stuff in dirty pink and Cambridge blue and buy a new three-piece suite. We put the carpet in and then bought the three-piece suite without first measuring the room, with the result that the sofa and chairs are

38

far too big. Visitors look like midgets, their little legs scarcely reaching the edge of the sofa, never mind touching the floor, as if they are participating in a surrealistic comedy by N.F. Simpson.

In the middle of this process my wife walked out for artistic reasons (she decided that a book I'd written was in deplorable taste), leaving me with a dirty-pink carpet, bottle-green curtains and a satirical three-piece suite. I've never had the heart to complete the renovations and judge anyway that the place is perfectly all right as long as the curtains are permanently drawn and all the lamps have orange bulbs.

'Look, madam,' I said to the crisp reporter, 'if it's good enough for Count Alvaro Domecq it's good enough for *Observer* readers.'

'This is Alvaro *Domecq's* town apartment?' she said.

I was becoming a little rattled, but I kept my head.

'No, bollock-brain,' I said. 'It's *my* town apartment, but the Count is coming to stay tomorrow.'

'Rather him than me,' she said. And then she left.

After she'd gone, I did wonder for the first time whether my new best friend, the Count, might be depressed by my circumstances – one aspect of his visit that hadn't bothered me in the least. I had assumed that, as a serious man, he wouldn't even notice them. It takes all sorts and so forth, and, as Justin Judd would say, a chap either stacks up or he doesn't – it's got nothing to do with décor. I have been sufficiently unnerved, however, to put red bulbs in the lamps instead of orange ones.

A Spaniard in the Works

Tony Walton, the set designer, once told me that he felt himself to be skating on thin ice, that he was confident he'd end up selling matches outside the Odeon, Leicester Square. In fact, he married Julie Andrews and has designed musicals all over the world, but I've no doubt he still expects the worst. I'm the same. For as long as I can remember I've been waiting for a knock on the door in the early morning, for burly men in pork-pie hats to take my stuff away.

People of this temperament have to cope as best they can with the imagined tidal wave of horror gathering strength outside. Ken the Australian Horse Player always carries a bar of soap in his top pocket and is ready to bite into it should he have his collar felt. The authorities, he calculates, will be reluctant to pot a hysteric who is foaming at the mouth, in case he kicks the bucket.

My French friend, Jean Leyris, worked out one day that all the people who want to get you into trouble trade only from nine to six, so he cut out office hours himself, rising in the late afternoon and packing it in at breakfast time. Accountants, VAT men and so forth scatched their heads and dropped off one by one.

Nearer home, we have a mad woman in the block who feeds the pigeons in her nightdress and trumpets abuse at anyone who dares to say that the pigeons droppings are causing the roof to collapse. I don't give a stuff about the roof, but I wouldn't go within a mile of her. I've never heard such language, and I'm a naval man. She won't have paid her poll tax, I imagine, but officious types from the town hall would be well advised to give her as wide a berth as I and the other tenants do.

Unfortunately, none of these evasive techniques quite suits me. I have to work during the day so Jean Leyris's solution isn't available to me; biting on a bar of soap is a bit too radical; and I haven't got the balls of the mad old tart who takes on all-comers in the yard.

I prefer a less confrontational approach – to maximize security, keep a low profile and hope for the best. I also have a pair of old folk's flannel pyjamas handy which I am ready to jump into should all else fail, thereafter curling up on the floor like a dead hedgehog. I reckon that burly men in pork-pie hats wouldn't harass a dead old codger in flannel jim-jams.

The truth is, security at my place is as tight as a fish's bum, and it's a further truth that if security's your game you don't pal up with a volatile, old-time Spaniard – which was precisely what I'd done, I realized, as I waited on Friday morning for my new best friend, Count Alvaro Domecq, to arrive for the weekend.

I say 'old-time' Spaniard since your new Spaniard – if my colleague Tim McGirk is to be believed – is a big girl's blouse, allowing you to insult his sister and backing away from fighting bulls. 'That animal wants to *kill*, me,' protested a matador called Rafael de Paula – according to McGirk – as he scampered from Madrid's bullring a week or two ago.

I tried to convince myself that my new best friend Alvaro might be like this, that he'd mind his p's and q's, keep a low profile and observe the security precautions. Not a chance. He arrived at my place on Friday morning wearing tights and armed to the teeth with ancestral weapons.

Keen, obviously, to introduce his country ways into my flat, he first tried to inflame my cats with Iberian insults, then to their surprise he stuck his bum out, clapped his hands and twirled in front of them, inviting them to charge. They eyed him haughtily, I'm glad to say, and then strolled off with the unhurried, contemptuous walk that only cats can muster.

'Where's the action?' Alvaro shouted, ready now to fight anything that moved.

Did he want to saddle up some naughty girls and gallop them round my flat, or would he prefer to attend a dog fight in Essex, jump into the ring himself and, to the mortification of their gnarled Cockney trainers, ponce and pirouette among the pit bull terriers, slashing them to ribbons with his spurs?

I had to go to work and since I didn't fancy a visit in my absence from the RSPCA I sat him down and told him to behave himself, to watch the World Cup on the television (if England were playing he might die laughing), and not, above all, to answer the door or telephone.

I spent a jumpy day at Mark Chapman's office, but when I got home all was peace and quiet and the Count was nowhere to be seen. I did find a note from him, however.

Disobeying my instructions he'd answered the telephone, it seemed, to my ex-second-best friend, Val Hennessy, and had been instantly ignited by a scorching volley of abuse meant for me. Judging that Hennessy would make a fierier weekend combatant he'd moved in with her, the note said, first making me a paella which I'd find in the kitchen.

So everything ended happily after all. Two of the cats are missing, but I expect they'll turn up soon.

41

Redirected to the Tradesmen's Entrance

Having worked at the *Daily Mail* and the *Mail on Sunday*, I am accustomed to being redirected to the tradesmen's entrance when calling on my social betters, but it still startles me a little every time it happens.

It happened on Saturday, in fact, when a group of us from Mark Chapman's office – together with my former second-best friend, Val Hennessy, and her new house guest (lately mine) Count Alvaro Domecq – drove to Norfolk in a bus to attend the wedding of Justin Judd and Emma Laybourne.

In excellent spirits and looking good, I think – myself in a City pinstripe and Old Etonian tie (having judged that my Old Wykehamist number was a little too garish on the day); Count Alvaro in ballet pumps and a matador's suit of lights; Chapman in green; Jane Lighting, his beloved, heartbreakingly beautiful in Oxford blue; the other girls (Jenny Zamit, Rachel Salter, Catey Sexton, and Jeremy Lovering) looking quite enchanting in their individual ways – we hopped out of the bus, carrying our little presents, and were headed off by a starchy retainer who, taking us to be the cabaret, I suppose, directed us to the artistes' entrance.

Water off a duck's back to 'Scoop' Donaldson – who, as the *Mail on Sunday*'s diarist, the pockets of my dirty raincoat stuffed with fivers in case I met a source, had been redirected to the servants' quarters at all our better homes – but the others took it rather badly. Jenny, a vision of loveliness in white, stamped her foot and stormed: 'I happen to be an Arsenal supporter. And I used to go out what's more, with "Chippy" Brady.'

This was a clinching reference in my book, but it didn't cut much ice with the starchy retainer. Then Count Alvaro stamped *his* foot, did a pirouette or two and, unscabbarding his *banderillas*, skewered the family donkey in a field. Hennessy, meanwhile, had started to call the odds.

'I've never been so insulted!' she screeched.

That seemed unlikely, and foolishly I said as much – thereby bringing down on my own head an avalanche of ripe abuse, which did as little for our cause, I think, as Jenny's outburst had.

'We're in showbusiness,' I explained.

'I can see that,' the starchy retainer said. 'Round the back.'

We were trooping dejectedly in that direction when the old retainer, impressed, I imagine, by Count Alvaro's country manners, suddenly indicated that he could join the line-up of decent types and girls in hats queuing to congratulate the bride and groom.

Then he locked the rest of us in the pantry where, shortly, a plate of vol-au-vents was delivered to us, courtesy of Judd, together with a note which expressed his regret that we weren't suitable, with the exception of Count Alvaro, to meet his other friends.

'This is outrageous,' Chapman fumed. 'The count's acceptable and he's just speared the family donkey!'

'County folk,' Rachel explained. 'They like that sort of stuff – killing things and so forth. Firm but fair. Stern but stupid.' 'She's right,' I said. 'Face it – we don't stack up on a lawn.'

'Speak for yourself.' Chapman said.

That's exactly what I was doing, as it happened, and I was quite unalarmed to discover how far down the greasy pole of social acceptability I'd slipped.

Once I could have done all this, worn hired clothes with aplomb, known how to behave in a tent. Once I drove a sports car in British racing green, had the last waltz at Claridge's with the Lord Great Chamberlain's daughter, was affianced briefly to the future President of France's sister.

And once, with a nice girl, I left a lawn like this to honeymoon in the South of France where, because public schoolboys didn't then associate nice girls – let alone their wives – with monkey business, I read a pornographic book beside the pool at La Reserve Beaulieu, having first wrapped it in the cover of Kingsley Amis's recently published *Lucky Jim*.

Peter Ustinov, who happened to be walking by, stopped and said: '*Lucky Jim*, eh? May I have a look?' Having read a page or two, he handed it back without a word, but he may not have sampled Amis again, I think.

Those were the days . . . and now I was locked in a pantry with a group of class-war anarchists, one of whom – Chapman – now tried to sell me his lime-green wedding suit.

'How much?' I asked.

'Two hundred pounds,' he said.

'Three hundred pounds,' I said, 'but I won't go higher.'

'Two hundred and fifty pounds,' he said. I was becoming discouraged but I battled on.

'Four hundred pounds,' I said, 'and that's my final offer.'

'Okay,' he said.

Shortly after this we slipped away and returned with our tails between our legs to London, and on Monday I was repossessed by Moss Bros, a consequence of Chapman's lime-green suit being on contract hire. I had to laugh, was quite encouraged, actually, since the incident bodes well, I think, for our upcoming television series, *Henry Root Into Europe*. Chapman may not be a very good director, but his business acumen suggests that we'll come in under budget.

I'm Even Commoner Than Val

If you want property at a knocked down price, I suggest you get on to the people who own my block. My ex-second-best friend, Val Hennessy, has been driven out of her flat by her house guest (lately mine), Count Alvaro Domecq, and has come to live with me. As a result, the tone of the neighbourhood has gone for six. Leaseholders are accepting peanuts for their homes and are moving to Notting Hill and Hammersmith.

I am not too bothered myself since I'm as common as Hennessy, though this is a contention she disputes. The argument started soon after we were directed to the servants' quarters when we tried to attend the wedding, in Norfolk, of Justin Judd and Emma Laybourne. I told Hennessy that the incident hadn't upset me in the least, whereupon she argued that this was because I was upper class and therefore confident enough to take such setbacks. I insisted that, on the contrary, I was as common as her, the only difference being that, whereas she had always been common (none commoner, perhaps), I had achieved commonness and was capable of acts of vulgarity which even she might balk at. The upshot was that we struck a bet of £500, the kitty going to the one who, by the end of the week, was able to do something so tasteless that the other was forced to concede.

On the face of it, Hennessy is much commoner than I am. My tastes and activities aren't common in the least, but I was relying on Hennessy being so common that she didn't realize this. In her favour (or in mine, rather) was that she reads the *Daily Mail*, writes for it to boot, and drinks dry white wine while composing her weekly piece. This struck me as so common that I kicked an own goal by telling her as much.

'Good God, Hennessy,' I said, 'only call girls drink dry white wine while working.'

'There you are,' she said. 'I'm as common as a call girl.'

I recovered quickly. 'Call girls aren't common,' I said. 'I've never met a common call girl in my life.' This wasn't quite true. Big Elaine, who used to live here, who bought her underwear through the post and who banked with the Abbey National, was as common as anyone I've ever met – but Hennessy was unaware of this and now bowed to my superior knowledge.

She then claimed points because I read the *Sun* each day. There's nothing common about reading the *Sun*, of course, but I was relying on Hennessy not knowing this. I take it, in fact, for its editorial content, but I told Hennessy that I liked to look at the page three lovelies over breakfast, confident that this admission would elicit a torrent of vulgarity. Predictably, she charged me with sexism and said that pictures of naked girls were an insult, if you please, to women – an exceptionally common point of view and one expressed these days only by people such as Muriel Gray. She then recovered slightly by watching the World Cup on television, becoming quite excited by the barrel-thighed Nellies on view feigning injury and hitting one another with their handbags.

She then did even better by suggesting that 'we eat Chinese', but I caught up by taking her to Big'Uns in Oxford Street, where I insisted that we 'go Dutch'. She then did well, however, by guzzling my starter (potted shrimps), which neither of us wanted, simply because it was included in the set price. Realizing that I must come up with something good, I started to boast about my time as a *marinero* on a Spanish tourist boat.

'One day,' I said, 'a very grand Spanish family commissioned us to take them lobster fishing. After the catch, we went to a secluded beach where the *capitano*, who was an excellent cook, made lunch. The *grandees* stuffed themselves at one end of the beach while the *capitano* and I sat humbly at the other. After they'd had enough, the *grandees* sent over a few scraps – shells merely – for us to suck on.'

'Did you mind?' asked Hennessy.

'Not in the least,' I said – realizing even as I spoke that I was about to kick another own goal. 'I knew my place.'

'That's because you're upper class,' said Hennessy. 'I've definitely won the bet.'

I refused to concede and I'm glad I didn't because, on Wednesday, I agreed to write the biography of Janie Jones, the delightful but extremely common madam. Nothing could be commoner, I thought, than to put back to square one, indeed, strip of their anonymity, the well-born chaps who took advantage of her services and then gave evidence against her. I spent the day listening to Janie's common anecdotes (of which more next week) and returned home to be told by Hennessy that she'd won the bet hands down. The mad old tart who feeds the pigeons in her nightdress and repels all who rebuke her with a volley of disgusting language, had put her flat on the market because she was unable to tolerate Hennessy's behaviour any longer.

I've had the last laugh, however. To Hennessy's astonishment I've refused to pay. I knew I'd come up with something commoner than she could manage.

And Janie Jones is Commoner Than Me

My colleague Paul Foot was unimpressed by the evidence mustered here last week to support my claim that I am commoner

46

than my ex-second-best friend, Val Hennessy. He tells me that in 1974 he was fined £500 for being common. I'd forgotten this, I must admit. Outraged that a crew of well-born deviants was allowed to appear in court as letters of the alphabet against our mutual friend Janie Jones – the jolly but extremely common madam – he named one of them (a member of the House of Lords and a relation, as it happens, of Her Majesty) in the *Socialist Worker* and was potted by Lord Chief Justice for contempt of court. 'I was lucky not to go to prison as a class traitor,' Foot told me on the telephone.

Meanwhile, there's a game of musical apartments going on between me, Janie Jones and Val Hennessy. We're juggling two properties between the three of us and the present state of play is that Hennessy has installed herself at my place and won't leave until I pay out on the bet we struck as to which of us is commoner. In self-defence, I've moved in with Janie and it's just as well I didn't make the bet with her. She's commoner than me, Hennessy and Paul Foot put together – indeed, she went to prison for being common in 1975, shortly after Foot was fined for the same offence. Some rude old poop on the bench said that she was the commonest woman he'd ever had to sentence and then he banged her up for seven years.

I took up residence with Janie as much to work on her biography as to get away from Hennessy, and I'd hoped for a bit of fun as well. Alas, Janie lives like a nun these days – though not like the six novices of the Carmelite Order to whom she has let several floors of her spacious property. The nuns leave the house at all hours in full theatrical make-up and – if the evidence on the washing line is to be believed – purchase their underwear at the novelty shop where Big Elaine (mentioned here last week) buys hers. Neither Janie nor I is of a religious cast of mind, so there's nothing for it but to work, watched over by Janie's extremely common literary agent, Burnette Rigg, a Gorbals tearaway who nuts commissioning editors who disagree with him and who interrupts our efforts by filing scoops on his mobile phone. Next week he is to auction our work among common publishers of whom, luckily, there appears to be no shortage.

Janie's story is extraordinary, I must say – a paradigm of hypocrisy and double standards (on the part of the authorities at least) – and my motivation in helping her to write it is, as I said last week, to put back to square one, indeed to strip of their anonymity, the upper-class gents who availed themselves of her services and then gave evidence against her. Just why the police – who normally smile benignly on the activities of far more successful madams than Janie ever was – were so keen to nail her is something of a mystery, but the answer lies, I think, in the way she ran her business. The police like madams to be respectable, to let them know what's going on and to ask them to their parties, but Janie was a nuisance, driving round in a pink Rolls-Royce, making pop records and consistently refusing to invite the Vice Squad to her weekly showbiz dos at which the likes of Tom Jones and Humperdinck disported themselves quite innocently while a fat woman danced with a rat on her head and nice old parties like me kidded ourselves that we were part of the *dolce vita*.

Her first brush with the law came in 1967 when the police arrived with the evidence one night and accused her of running a brothel. They then cut corners with even more affrontery than usual – claiming that several American Air Force officers had visited her house during a weekend when, in fact, her mother had been staying with her, further stating that they had observed the imaginary comings and goings from a balcony which had not at the time been built. This was too much even for a British judge to swallow and Janie was acquitted.

The police took this setback badly and arrested her a few years later on a cooked-up blackmail charge. The evidence on this occasion was provided by Mr A, a dossy old peer (named by Paul Foot) whose taste for fourteen year-old schoolgirls had been kept in check by Janie who, for several years, had been supplying him with over-the-hill actresses. Most of them were in their forties, but Mr A never twigged. One of the more resourceful ones suggested once that she should bring her mother with her, later pitching up with a colleague half her age. Mr A was thrilled. On another occasion she said that she had a twin sister, left for ten minutes and then got paid twice by coming back under a different name. Mr A was delighted. 'You're much prettier than your sister,' he said.

Mr A's evidence was treated with the contempt it deserved and once again Janie was acquitted. This annoyed the judge so much that he gave her seven years anyway – which seems a bit steep for something you didn't do. Four years would have been par for the course, I'd have thought.

Lunchtime O'Mount and a Conservative Giraffe

The distinguished cartoonist Michael Heath may have suffered a blow to his reputation in Stoke, I think – and the fault is undoubtedly mine. Keen to win this year's Twyford's Prize for Toilet Books, he and I came up some months ago with *1992 and All That* – a collection of slightly silly jokes about our European neighbours and, indeed, about ourselves. Since I've taken a year off from writing books to concentrate on journalism we agreed that, on this occasion, he'd write the book and I'd do the cartoons. The results, as you might expect, are excellent and the book is scorching up the charts.

Such has been the interest, in fact, that for the past few days I have been bruising round the country publicising the thing on radio, ending up in Stoke, talking to a disc jockey called Dave.

It's always hard work talking to a disc jockey about a book he hasn't read; even harder when you haven't written it – or read it, either, come to that. Dave, who had the book in front of him, bowled me a beamer immediately by reading out a sample of Heath's jokes and then asking me to comment.

'Here's one,' he said. '"Bus conductors in Naples get a bonus each month if they refrain from hitting the passengers."'

'Screamingly funny,' I said.

'Yes, but is it true?'

'You've got me there, Dave,' I said.

Dave wasn't satisfied. 'What about this one,' he said. '"After Jan Molby, the Danish footballer, had been playing for Liverpool for a week, he was asked on local radio what had been his greatest difficulty in settling in. 'The language barrier,' said Molby. 'You mean the lads can't speak Danish?' said the interviewer. 'No,' said Molby. 'They can't speak English. Least of all

49

the boss, Mr Dalglish.' Molby was fined £200 for bringing the game into disrepute." I can't believe that. Is the book a fiction?'

'It can't be,' I said. 'I'm too stupid to make things up. No imagination, do you see?'

Dave squinted at me suspiciously and then changed the subject, asking me my opinion of last week's *Spectator* bombshell. I did have an attitude to this, fortunately, taking the view that while the article had been a scandal it should not occasion, for the second time in a few years, A.N. Wilson's resignation as the paper's temporary literary editor – and I said as much to Dave.

'The piece was an outrage,' I said. 'But I don't think A.N. Wilson should resign.'

'I wasn't talking about A.N. Wilson's conversation with the Queen Mother,' said Dave.

'Nor was I,' I said. 'I was referring – as I assumed you were – to Ferdinand Mount's impertinent review of Professor Ted Honderich's important new book, *Conservatism*, in which Mount made languid jokes about the Professor's wardrobe and, indeed, his name, at one point taking issue with Honderich's insistence that Conservatives should have some 'general principle', or they would not be recognizable to themselves and to others.

'"What," asks Mount absurdly, "is the general principle of a giraffe?" None whatsoever, of course, but a theory could reasonably be expected of a Conservative giraffe – a point that should not be too complicated for the languorous Mr Mount to grasp. If the piece was written by Mount, that is. I suspect in fact that A.N. Wilson gave the book to my friend Wallace Arnold to review and that he then mischievously switched bylines.'

Dave looked baffled and said that he had been referring to Dominic Lawson's interview with Nicholas Ridley and to its repercussions.

'A storm in a teacup,' I said. 'I've just spent six weeks in Europe and I can tell you that we are looked upon there as buffoons and hypocrites, and light years off the pace. Take our attitude to pornography, for instance. Val Hennessy . . .'

'Who's she?' said Dave.

'A very difficult woman who has installed herself at my place and upset my local newsagent by covering his display of erotic magazines with unsold copies of the *Daily Mail*. When I rebuke her she says that such material insults women and causes them to walk in fear. I explain that the EC countries with the most liberal laws relating to pornography have the lowest figures for rape and indecent assault, but Hennessy isn't impressed.'

Nor was Dave. His expression of amused forbearance was so insulting that I heard myself quoting from a confidential talk I'd been privileged to have in Italy with Giovanni Falcone, Palermo's chief investigating magistrate. England, Falcone told me, was the only EC country that wouldn't co-operate with him in his war against the Mafia. When he informs Scotland Yard that twenty Mafia dons are staying at the London Hilton, some plod laughs at him and says that the Mafia doesn't exist.

'We're idiots,' I said.

'Thank you,' said Dave. 'I have been talking to Michael Heath who has some very odd views about pornography and the Mafia, who has no imagination, who is too stupid to make things up and who lives with Val Hennessy. Good night.'

Garry Bushell and Professor Honderich

An intellectually confusing week in which my friend Garry Bushell of the *Sun* joined the exciting campaign to legalize hard drugs, and Ted Honderich, Grote Professor of Mind and Logic at University College, London, persuaded me, I think, that my sister Bobo's opposition to Garry libertarian opinion is only dubiously moral.

In his article in Monday's *Sun* Garry, as you will remember, relied on straightforwardly consequentialist arguments suggesting, conventionally enough, that the drug problem could best be solved not by fatuous activity by customs and excise officers, but by making a legal supply available to anyone stupid enough to want the stuff. Gangsters, Garry argued, would no longer be able to prey on impressionable young people and the upshot would be a decrease in addiction. I'm not convinced of this, in fact, and have discovered anyway that apparently irrefutable

51

arguments of this sort don't cut any ice with Mrs Thatcher and my sister Bobo – so I rang up Garry and told him as much.

'If you have lunch with my sister Bobo,' I said, 'you'll find that she is remarkably unimpressed by consequentialist arguments, as is Mrs Thatcher, I imagine. In this area, as in certain others (pornography and capital punishment come to mind), Mrs Thatcher and my sister Bobo are deaf to arguments of this sort.

'Confronted by the latest addiction figures from Amsterdam (which proved beyond doubt that libertarian policies work), Bobo says: "Who'd want to live in Amsterdam anyway?" Nor does it seem to me that her position is obviously irrational. Nothing could be easier than to manufacture traps for the unwary utilitarian. It is not clear, for instance, that everyone would want to live in a society which, by compelling its citizens to watch unimaginably obscene films on television, had rid itself of all forms of sexual violence.

'Equally, there seems little doubt that the mad women who rattle handcuffs at the Consevative Party conference and squeal excitedly for the return of the rope do so not because they seriously believe that capital punishment is a deterrent, but because they *like* it (just as decent people would oppose its reintroduction even if it were shown that its absence would cause the murder rate to soar). Are you with me?'

Garry said that he was with me all the way and that if I cared to get off the phone he'd be able to ring my sister Bobo and suggest a lunchtime rendezvous – at which he expected, by the force and lucidity of his arguments, to prevail where I'd hit fog.

I wished him well, then wondered why, if it were a question of alcohol being banned, I'd be as deaf to arguments as Bobo is when the legalization of other, possibly less harmful, intoxicants is mooted. While recognizing that the prohibition of alcohol would cause a vast increase in human misery, I'd still be more comfortable in a society in which the stuff was banned and consumption of other drugs encouraged.

No one, surely, whose preferred intoxicant for any length of time had not been alcohol would do Humphrey Bogart impressions in a wine bar or appear smirkingly in a comical televised news quiz; speak in a restaurant on a mobile phone or participate in tights at the Publishers Association annual pantomine; say silly sweaty things to girls or, as an older woman at her daughter's wedding, hitch up her skirt and tapdance on a table; make an after-dinner speech, put a fellow citizen behind bars for eight years for supplying a member of the Royal Family with *her* preferred intoxicant or, most tellingly perhaps, look, talk or otherwise behave like David Waddington, Jeremy Beadle or the Lord Chief Justice.

Then wondering whether my preference for a society free of such embarrassments was merely a matter of taste – that arguments in its favour would be aesthetic rather than moral – I decided to check the matter out with Professor Honderich.

'Quite possibly,' he said. 'Consider a man who argues that the fundamental moral principle is to maximize the colour mauve. Under questioning he admits that mauve doesn't make people happy, issue in fairness or whatever, but maintains that one should maximize it nonetheless just because it is intrisically good. Such a moral principle would seem incredible; indeed, it is difficult to see that it is a moral principle at all.

'However, it is not obvious what stands between it and any non-consequentialist principle – for instance, that one should always act out of the purist conscience or according to the will of God. They seem as dubiously moral as your arguments for banning alcohol – not that you've offered any.'

That seemed fair and I rang Garry to see how he'd got on with Bobo. 'You were right,' he said. 'She's like a man who – to use an analogy I once constructed for Professor Honderich – argues that the fundamental moral principle is to maximize the colour mauve. Under questioning this man . . .'

Well I never. Next time I won't trouble Professor Honderich; I'll get straight on to Garry.

The Queen's Behind With Her Correspondence

Tony the Drug Fiend, whom I visited on Friday in Maidstone Prison, hasn't had a reply yet to a perfectly sensible letter he wrote to the Queen at least six months ago. Annoyed that he was doing eight years for supplying one of her younger relatives with controlled substances he delicately suggested that, since he had been cool enough to keep mum at his trial about the younger relative's habit, she, the Queen, should now pitch in on his behalf, supporting his application for parole – and, as I say, he hasn't heard a dickie bird. I appreciate that Her Majesty must get a lot of this stuff over breakfast but a brief acknowledgement would surely have been in order.

For this discourtesy I rather blame her parents. This may seem unfair but I'm in the mood at the moment to blame parents for almost everything, toiling away as I am on my autobiography, *From Sunningdale to This*, in which I slice my childhood pretty thin.

Responsibility for the moderate hash I've made of things can, I think, be laid at my parents' door. My mother, typically, enforced love as if by contract, used me as a weapon against my father who had disappointed her, and gave me to understand that I should take as my example *her* father, a teak-stern patriarch who had once had a rugger trial for England. To hurt my father she enrolled me in the hearties' house at Winchester and, in order that I shouldn't let her down, hired international sportsmen to coach me in the holidays.

Later, when called upon to do my national service in the Navy, I didn't want to join immediately since I had just begun to do the season and was in love, I thought, with the Lord Great Chamberlain's daughter, so my mother rang up the First Sea Lord and told him that he couldn't have me yet. His Lordship, realizing that he'd met his match, said I could pitch up when it suited.

It's a wonder in a way that I've turned out as well as I have. Be that as it may, I'd done enough, I thought, on the sinister love of parents for their children, but visiting Tony the Drug Fiend in Maidstone Prison made me think the whole thing through again. Why, I wondered, had he turned out so well compared to me?

I'm not referring, of course, to his worldly achievements, impressive as these are. At the time of his arrest he had two properties in Ireland, a row of cottages in the South of France and, after paying a fine of £50,000, he still had £160,000 in off-shore banks – nothing to write home about compared to the

54

accumulated loot of dealers in more lethal intoxicants such as Guinness and Distillers, but not bad for a boy who left school at the age of twelve and who, until landing up in Maidstone, had never learnt to read or write.

That's trivial stuff and I'm referring, in fact, to his sweetness of nature and to the general excellence of his character, to the fortitude which has meant that the sadistic half-wit who locked him up for eight years has not been able to break his spirit.

As we talked across a table in the bleak visiting room it occurred to me that I'd only ever come across one other person who was as balanced, as trusting and as optimistic.

When I met my literary agent, Alison, it struck me almost immediately that there was something odd about her, that she didn't bring to every situation a nervy history of setbacks and imagined insults, that, trusting almost everyone, she expected them to trust her – which they usually did.

'There's something odd about you,' I said to her one day. 'I can't figure it out.'

'I'm happy,' she said.

I'd never heard anyone say such a thing before. I asked her why this was and she said she didn't know, but several conversations later I discovered that, at the age of fourteen – and tired of her role in her parents' private war – she had packed all her belongings into a suitcase one afternoon and had struggled down the road to her grandparents' house, thereafter quietly moving in with them.

Since they no longer had the need to recreate their lives through her, they loved her sensibly, caring for her as one would an important pet – offering warmth, food and the occasional necessary cuddle – and as a result my literary agent, Alison, is as brave, as affectionate and as independent as a well-brought-up pussycat. Undamaged by imperial parental love, she threatens no one, since no one has ever threatened her.

Sitting across the visitors' table in Maidstone Prison I asked Tony the Drug Fiend who had raised him.

'My grandmother,' he said.

I wasn't surprised. It's a shame, though, that the Queen didn't have the same good fortune, in which case she might not be behind now with her correspondence.

Blacker on Horseback

According to an old Fleet Street theory, there should be one page in any newspaper — whole sections, I imagine, in the *Sunday Times* — which no one reads. 'Ah! Food and Travel. Don't have to read that. What a relief.' That the *Independent's* duff page might be this one occurred to me a week or two ago when I absent-mindedly published here an old and delightfully incoherent column by Jeffrey Bernard and no one noticed. Happily, a colossal postbag after I described my religious experience after taking Ecstasy, suggests that if the *Independent* does keep one page blank, it isn't this one.

Most of my correspondents asked me to explain Dummett's argument from value (which I'd assumed was familier to *Independent* readers). Some were more interested in the continuing effects of my experience. Writing from Devizes, and quoting William James (*Varieties of Religious Experience*, Fontana), Canon Peter Entwistle said that a radical change in my behaviour since the experience would point to a divine explanation. 'God is real,' he wrote, 'because He has real effects.'

My behaviour *has* changed since the experience and I was sufficiently rattled by Canon Entwistle's argument to check for an immediate tutorial with my best friend, Little Jo, who is features editor of *Ritz*. She is so clever that her brain sticks out of her head, a circumstance which in no way stops her attending style and fashion shoots. Over lunch, I came straight to the point.

'Look here, Little Jo,' I said. 'God is real because He has real effects. What do you make of that?'

'Not a lot,' she said, putting on her spectacles. 'It's a very weak argument, due to James, I rather think. The fact that people often behave differently after a religious experience in no way shows that the experience had a divine cause. Such a claim would be to equate the truth of a belief with its power to motivate.'

'Thank you,' I said.

'I haven't finished. The problem with the religious interpretation of religious experience is that it is quite deficient in explanatory power. The judgement that one has had a divine experience is entirely unlike the judgement that one has seen an elephant, say – or an Abominable Snowman or the Loch Ness Monster, even – in that it appears to lead to no testable, independent predictions.'

'What if I *could* predict further experiences of a religious sort? What if I continued to take Ecstasy?'

'I'd have to tell Daddy,' said Little Jo. 'And he'd say that I couldn't have lunch with you any more. What, anyway, are the continuing effects of your experience?'

I explained that I felt strangely purified and that I had an almost overwhelming desire to confess past misdeeds, to blow the whistle on myself.

'That's admirable,' said Little Jo.

'Indeed. But I have an even stronger compulsion to blow the whistle on everyone else. Entirely for their own good, of course. I had not previously realized, I must admit, that my friends Dempster, Ingrams, Rantzen and so forth are, when putting others in it, religiously motivated. Now I understand. I have, like them, become a moral watchdog. No one's safe.'

'Who's first in the frame?' asked Little Jo.

'My friend Terence Blacker, I'm afraid. A week or two ago he rang me in a frightful stew. In a moment of folly he had suggested to the literary editor of the *Sunday Times* that he submit a think-piece deploring ageism in publishing. It was outrageous, he'd argue in this essay, that publishers only wanted first novels by pretty twenty-year-olds. A first novel by a fifty-five-year-old, he'd say, would be of greater interest.'

'What was his problem?'

'The article had been commissioned but he could no longer remember why he had thought it a good idea. Brain gone, do you see?'

'Not surprising at his age.'

'Precisely. Anyway, I couldn't help him. I agreed with the publishers, I said. Who'd want to read a first novel by an old plop? The enterprise, in all likelihood, would be embarrassing – like someone taking up expressionist dancing in their fifties – at once inhibited and frisky. Blacker grumbled a bit but he must have puzzled it out because the piece duly appeared last week, its thrust in a nutshell being that in literature, unlike fashion, age was irrelevant. Writers should write, Blacker argued, not pose in silly clothes for PR snaps. When I rang to congratulate him, he said he could not chat.

"'A glossy magazine is due here in five minutes to photograph me with my horse," he said. "You haven't got a horse," I said. "The horse," he said, "is to be provided by the PR firm promoting my brilliant first novel *Fixx*. I'm to be sold as The Balladeer on Horseback.'"

'Good heavens,' said Little Jo.

'Exactly. I said that the new me would have to expose him as a fraud. He begged me not to, but I said it was for his own good.'

'I'm with Blacker,' said Little Jo. 'The glossy magazine was *Ritz* and the horse idea was mine. Promise you won't write about it?'

'All right,' I said.

Alas, my religious instincts have got the better of me.

Mrs Mouse and Ronnie Lott

When, in 1970, Mrs Mouse and I sold our penthouse in the King's Road and moved to Ibiza, we stored all our stuff with two chaps from *Yellow Pages*. Three years later we couldn't remember their names, so a couple of wide-awake characters with a garage in south London must still believe that Christmas arrives early from time to time. Easy come, easy go, I thought, but now, through an equally silly mishap, I've just lost everything again and on Tuesday at the Garrick I was telling them as much.

The talk until then had all been of vandalized skylines and of infelicities in written and spoken English (the *Independent on Sunday*, it had been argued, must already be counted as the highest selling quality Sunday newspaper on the grounds that the *Sunday Times* could no longer lay a serious claim to inclusion in this category), so I dozed off, waking up after an hour or so and announcing that, because I am in love with Ronnie Lott, two burly men in pork-pie hats had recently walked off with all my goods which later fetched exactly £749 at a repossession sale. Not very much money these days, I said, still less when you took into account the fact that, without a television set which belonged to DER and a washing-machine loaned to me by

Professor O'Hear of Bradford University, the sum raised would have been a pitiful £211.86p.

'Who the fuck,' said Peregrine Worsthorne, 'is Ronnie Lott?'

I was as knocked back as you'd have been. This was not a slapstick journalist speaking, but the sometime trustee of a distinguished editorial chair, a heavyweight, a man on terms with men of affairs and archbishops, no mere commentator on great events but an actor in them – and yet he hadn't heard of Ronnie Lott.

I was, frankly, too stunned to speak, but my friend Geoffrey Wheatcroft was able, happily, to fill in for me.

'Ronnie Lott,' he said, 'is the finest free-safety in the National Football League. Carrying out some experiments recently with blocks, tackles and sacks of wet cement on a neighbour's smallholding, John Taylor, Professor of Mathematics at London University, discovered that when Lott, moving at 26mph, unloads on a running-back who is travelling in the opposite direction at the same speed, the impact is that of a medium-sized wrecking-ball hitting a pigsty from a distance of fifteen yards.

'Ask Ickey Woods, the Cincinatti Bengals' high-stepping fullback and the spearhead of their rushing game. Early in the first quarter of Super Bowl XXIII, Lott, you may remember, hit Ickey like a dumptruck. Ickey there after didn't want to know and the 49ers' offence – Montana, Rice, Craig and so forth – were able to win the game for San Francisco. Pass the port.'

Worsthorne said he was most obliged but none the wiser as to what this had to do with the fact that I'd just lost all my possessions.

'Some months ago,' I said, 'I discovered that by installing one of Rupert Murdoch's dishes I could watch several games of American football in a week, many of them featuring Ronnie Lott with whom, as I say, I am in love. I went to Winchester, do you see?'

'Of course.'

'My application for a dish was opposed by my fusspot of a neighbour – a vaguely bookish man with thin legs and a place in Tuscany, I wouldn't wonder – on the farcical grounds that such an installation would deface the skyline. I beat him hands down, of course, but I decided none the less to get my revenge should the opportunity arise.

'One morning last week, I received a notice from the Gas Board informing me that they had a warrant to enter my premises and discontinue my supply. Since I was going out to lunch that day – and not wishing this to happen in my absence – I found a screwdriver and, quite resourcefully I think, switched the number plates on my neighbour's door with mine. And it was just as well I did. When I got back from lunch I was accosted by my neighbour who wanted to know if he could use my bath since his gas had been cut off.

'I had to laugh, and was still laughing a few minutes later when I bumped into these two burly chaps in pork-pie hats taking the last of my possessions out of my flat. 'Glad to see someone isn't trying to keep up with the Joneses,' one of them said. My damn fool neighbour hadn't paid his polltax if you please, and these were the bailiffs here to take his stuff away. I told them they were in the wrong flat, but they wouldn't see reason and now I've lost everything.'

'What a distressing story,' said Worsthorne.

'Not really,' I said. 'The only items of value were the television set belonging to DER and the washing-maching loaned to me by Professor O'Hear. The Habitat furniture was no great shakes and, had I been able to afford the removal charge, I'd have ditched it years ago. They didn't get my dish and, since I've hired another television set from DER, I can still sit on the floor and watch Ronnie Lott into the small hours.'

Little Jo Gets Her Chance with Sneaks & Co

Soon after Sir Robert Mark became Commissioner of the Metropolitan Police I asked him if he was serious in his ambition to rid the force of its rotten apples. When he said he was, I suggested that such a scheme might prove impractical since it would require him to police the capital on his own. I can't remember his reply and I'd forgotten the incident until this week when, on behalf of Sneaks and Co., I attended a meeting of the Association of Investigative Journalists (common informers to you and me) at which ways were discussed whereby the association might improve its image.

In a beefy speech from the top table our president, Ian Hislop of *Private Eye*, proposed that members who were not irreproachably virtuous in their personal habits should be dismissed and it was at this point that I remembered my conversation with Sir Robert.

If such a motion were carried, I said, Richard Ingrams, the doyen of informers and as morally idiosyncratic in this field as Sir Robert had been in his, would be forced out of retirement to monitor the behaviour of others on his own. I added that if evidence were needed to support this proposition a glance round the room would yield as remarkable a collection of toe-rags and chancers as had ever met simultaneously in one place.

This was taken to be a facetious intervention and I was then quizzed from the chair about my next scoop. With the help of Tony the Drug Fiend, I said, I was about to pot a cross-section of his former clients, not least a relative of the Queen and certain younger members of the aristocracy. The president tut-tutted and then suggested that, since my own foothold on the moral uplands was noticeably insecure, I had disqualified myself from publishing hot potatoes – for all the world as if it wasn't in the public's interest to know who was misbehaving if the source was another ratbag.

I then left, regretting that I hadn't informed the assembled self-righteous gossips that it was only after I'd had a religious experience myself that I felt morally obliged to get others into trouble. I wasn't guilty of this overnight, however, when I had lunch the next day with my best friend, Little Jo, who has recently been pressing her suitability as a Sneaks and Co. operative with a vigour that in anyone else might be undignified. Little Jo, as I've said before, is so clever that her brain sticks out of her head – by no means a necessary condition in itself for joining Sneaks and Co. but not much of a disadvantage when coupled with another of her attributes – a willingness, in spite of her enormous brain, to keep in touch with types who dance in tents, drive to Windsor for the last race in a convoy of Jeeps and on the way fire champagne corks at members of the working class.

Wired for sound under her cocktail frock she could do the little season on behalf of Sneaks and Co., I said, reporting misdemeanours witnessed – not least those committed by old Lord Whatsit's boy who, according to Tony the Drug Fiend, is back on the stuff in spite of the best efforts of cold-eyed Christians in rehabilitation clinics.

'I couldn't do that,' said Little Jo. 'He's a *friend* of mine!'

'Exactly,' I said. 'Like a mafia recruit making his bones, you must demonstrate your loyalty to Sneaks and Co. by betraying the trust of an intimate.'

'My religion wouldn't allow me to,' said Little Jo.

'Don't give me religion,' I said. 'You forget that it was only after I had a religious experience in Ibiza that I became a moral watchdog.'

'I haven't forgotten,' said Little Jo, putting on her specs and looking stern, 'and what I said at the time still holds: a change in behaviour after a religious experience says nothing about a divine cause. Such a claim would be to equate the truth of a belief with its power to motivate.'

'Nevertheless,' I said, 'I *was* suddenly convinced that Dummett's argument from value to a transcendent being was obviously sound. I therefore blew the whistle on my friend Terence Blacker who, days after writing an article in which he deplored serious novelists who indulge in PR antics, sang "Don't Fence Me In", in public on a horse.'

'You were right to do that and no mistake,' said Little Jo. 'Okay, I'll grass up old Lord Whatsit's boy.'

And it's only now I realize that, by writing this, I've blown her cover, perhaps condemning her to the fate reserved for canaries that sing. Never mind. In at the deep end and so forth and, if she survives, she might help me with another of my scoops. Black Dominique tells me that the real king of Spain is as black as your hat and is being held at Her Majesty's pleasure in a Park Lane apartment, guarded by SAS men. We plan to snatch him, thereafter debriefing him in a Sneaks and Co. safe-house where Little Jo – who knows a king when she sees one – will suss him out in no time. If he stands up, we'll fly him to Spain where we'll confront the imposter, Juan Carlos. 'Bad news, my man. You're not the only king running around, you know.' More on this next week.

Black Dominique and the King of Spain

It's the small details that make a story stack up. I was finally convinced that the real King of Spain is as black as your hat and being held at Her Majesty's pleasure in a Park Lane apartment when Black Dominique – the brains behind Sneaks and Co.'s plans to snatch him – revealed that he wears little slippers with the Spanish royal crest on them and that his bona fides have been checked out by Sandy Gall's wife, Eleanor. Sandy Gall isn't the sort of man whose wife would easily swallow any old black man's claim that he's the King of Spain.

The coup was postponed for a couple of weeks because Black Dominique wanted time to get her head together. Time is money, however, so I rang her on Monday to see if she'd got her head together yet and, when she said she had, I asked her what was holding us up.

'I am waiting to hear from my opposite number in Morocco,' she said. That made sense, so I rang off – and then I thought, no it doesn't, so I rang back and asked her what the caper had to do with her opposite number in Morocco, whoever he or she might be.

'For political reasons,' said Black Dominique, 'Clarence has decided that our man should be flown to Morocco in a diplomatic bag. We'll give him to King Hussein.'

This was a new development; hitherto we'd planned to pop up unexpectedly in Spain where we'd confront the imposter, Juan Carlos. ('Bad news, my man. You're not the only king running around you know.') And who was Clarence? 'Clarence works for BP,' said Black Dominique. 'Unfortunately, he's just suffered a bereavement. His aunt came over from Trinidad last week. She went up to the bathroom and dropped down dead. Very sad.'

Very sad indeed, but business is business and while it was reasonable to hold things up so that Black Dominique could get her head together it made no sense, as far as I could see, to kick our heels just because Clarence's aunt had dropped down dead in the bathroom.

Was I about to involve Sneaks and Co. in its first fiasco? I had a

63

duty, after all, to my fellow directors – Honest John, who is currently in the doghouse for confusing news-gathering with news creation; Little Jo, who, wired for sound under her cocktail frock, is tailing old Lord Whatsit's boy from one society do to another; and Jillypoo, who has wheels and a filthy temper and will therefore protect the rest of us if things get naughty out on the cobbles – and I had a duty, too, to the various tabloid journalists who now rely entirely on it Sneaks and Co. for information.

Every morning, representatives from the *Sun* and so forth – men with neat little feet and heads like racing tadpoles – ring me up and ask what's going on.

I tell them tales that make them gasp, none of which they believe, however, because, as they say, who would take the word of a common prostitute against that of a Tory MP?

Anyone with any sense, I say, since business girls, having no interest in sex (or sex, at least, with fat men who pay them), have neither the imagination nor the time to concoct fantasies in this department.

If a business girl tells you that a Tory MP likes to be pinned like a moth to her front door, thereafter instructing one of her colleagues to open the door with such force from the outside that he is flattened against the wall like a cartoon cat, you can put your holiday money on the story being true. It is punters who are as mad as hatters, I explained, not the business girls – but a lurking doubt made me re-check the facts.

'Let's get this straight,' I said. 'When our man – the future King of Spain – turns out to be as black as your hat, they instruct his nanny to dispose of him. Instead, she smuggles him to Nicaragua. Later he turns up at Windsor Castle where he is held at Her Majesty's pleasure.'

'That's right,' said Black Dominique. 'In the basement with the White Russians. And you know what Her Majesty's pleasure is – they keep you breathing. We should give the man a lifestyle.'

'So we should. And now he's in a Park Lane apartment guarded by SAS men. How do you know they're SAS?'

'They're 6ft 6in and serve the tea. On top of which he has a lifelong bus pass. I ask you – what's a black man doing living in a £2000-a-week apartment with a lifelong bus pass unless he's the King of Spain? And you're forgetting something else: Eleanor

Gall and I have seen his feet. He wears little slippers with the royal crest on them. We've got to move fast. They've got him doped to the eyeballs and plan to run him over as he crosses the road on his little legs. I've arranged tea with the Moroccan ambassador at the Kensington Hilton.'

That's no good. Sneaks and Co. won't make money if Black Dominique gets him to Morocco. We'll pitch up at the Kensington Hilton in Jillypoo's van and snatch him while he's taking tea. Jillypoo will smack the Moroccan ambassador and a couple of SAS types and then we'll auction him off at my place, or better still at Little Jo's. The man deserves a lifestyle after all.

Jillypoo, m'lud. Education and Home Affairs'

I hope my employers here don't twig that they and Jillypoo are standing bail for the King of Spain. And I'll say this for the authorities; they move like lightning when they have to. At 7 a.m. on Saturday, Clarence rang to say that within minutes of my world exclusive to the effect that the King of Spain was as black as your hat, His Majesty had been snatched by Them from his Park Lane flat and would be appearing in court in a couple of hours for unacceptable behaviour.

'Is that an offence?' I asked – rather stupidly, I now see. Clarence (my entrée to the King and known in royal circles as the Black Poet Laureate, but someone who for all that has his head screwed on) chuckled briefly at my naivety. 'And who's Them?' I said.

'The people who run the country,' Clarence said. 'I told you They'd get him.'

He then suggested that I should be present in court – either as myself or, better still, as the *Independent* – so that I could spring His Majesty, standing bail and giving my address as his since They had already put a padlock on the door of his Park Lane flat for unacceptable rent arrears, at the same time confiscating the last of the crown jewels which consisted now, Clarence said, of a pin with a ruby in it and the King's teeth which were fashioned out of gold and which he wore only on State occasions. I gathered, in fact, that His Majesty's unacceptable arrears included an instruction that all his bills should be sent directly to the Queen at Buckingham Palace who would settle them instantly in view of who he was.

Be that as it may, the plan stacked up as far as I could see so, availing myself of Jillypoo's wheels, I was in the foyer of the court at 9.30 – either as myself, or as a more senior representative from the *Independent* (I left the matter open) – where Clarence was persuading a quite sensible-seeming QC that his client was indeed HRH Prince Don Juan Alfonso, eldest son of King Alfonso the XIII and Queen Eugena Victoria.

'Because His Royal Highness was black,' Clarence explained, 'his nanny was told to dispose of him in a planned incident. Instead, she smuggled him to Nicaragua where he was protected by Somoza. Later he was brought to England where he was kept in the basement with the White Russians. While they weren't sure which way Franco would jump they treated him well, but when the imposter, Juan Carlos, was nominated king, they dropped him like a hot potato.

His business people were withdrawn and he then fell into the hands of hoodlums.'

'I see,' said the QC. 'Which hoodlums exactly?'

'Mrs Ferguson,' said Clarence. 'A black woman who considers herself to be at the pinnacle of Ealing society. Mrs Ferguson thought it wouldn't harm her socially to be seen running around Ealing with the King of Spain.'

'Of course not,' the QC said. 'So what is the most telling evidence you have that our man is who he claims to be?'

'I have a letter to myself from the Queen,' Clarence said. 'Reading between the lines, you'll see she's satisfied by his credentials.'

The QC glanced at the letter. 'I'm unclear why,' he said.

Clarence lost his temper. 'Get a grip on yourself, my man!' he screamed. 'If the Queen hadn't been convinced she'd have written "bullshit, Clarence!"'

The QC agreed, but suggested that if Clarence was so questioned by the magistrate he should moderate his answer. And he did. Moments later we were all in court and Clarence was asked why his letter from the Queen seemed to him to be such telling evidence. 'Because, m'lud,' said Clarence, 'if Her Majesty hadn't been convinced, she'd have written "leave it out, Clarence".'

The magistrate was impressed, and he was no less impressed, I think, when I took the stand myself.

'Who are you?' he said.

'The *Independent*,' I said.

The magistrate liked that, but he frowned a bit when I revealed I didn't own a house – or anything else, come to that. The day was saved by Jillypoo, however, who now stood up and said that she was happy to take the odds against our man pitching up when next required.

'And who are you?' the magistrate said.

'Jillypoo,' Jillypoo said. 'The *Independent*. Education and Home Affairs.'

'Do you own a house?' the magistrate said.

'No, m'lud,' Jillypoo said. 'But I have wheels.'

'That's more than your editor seems to have,' the magistrate said.

'Thank you, m'lud,' Jillypoo said. 'In the circumstances I'm prepared to slap a monkey down which says our man will appear next week. And I'll tell you this, m'lud; I'm sixty-forty he's the fucking king.'

The magistrate had come to the same conclusion, clearly, and His Royal Highness was released into my safekeeping. Not so safe, as it happens, since I have lost him already. I told him to pick up his laundry in Park Lane and I buzzed off in the opposite direction. I'm not stupid.

Nailed by the News of the World

If you fall in love with a reporter on the *News of the World* and if, on your first date, your door is kicked in by the police because they're looking for the King of Spain, you'll be lucky indeed if the bust is led by D.C. Dick (Mr Dick to me) – one of the most sophisticated young men you could meet in a long day's march.

Equally, if your personal life is so at sixes and sevens that it bears investigation by the Murdoch press, you'll be very fortunate if the reporter picked to nail you is Miss Sandie Laming who has a mind like a steel trap and the heart-breaking beauty of a Page Three Cracker.

The first fateful meeting with my beloved took place on Wednesday when Tony the Drug Fiend and I, as part of our campaign to expose hypocrisy and double standards (or, to express it differently, to make a bit of money by blowing the whistle on many of his former clients, including a relation of the Queen) took lunch with the *News of the World*. I don't know about you, but when I fall in love I don't seek courteously to draw the loved one out about herself or make my admiration clear by judicious flattery; for some reason I aim the compliments at myself and bring her swiftly up to date with my latest thinking on this and that. And so it was now with Sandie Laming.

'How do you do,' I said. 'This will interest you. When I was the *Mail on Sunday*'s gossip columnist, my friend Sir David English urged me to write about adulterers and so forth, but I refused. This would be common informing, I said, for which lapse of taste perpetrators were, in my circle at least, customarily planted upside down in wet cement.

'On the other hand,' I said, 'no one could object to lies and distortions about themselves, or sue over an obvious joke. I therefore wrote that Nigel Dempster, returning home the worse for wear one night, thoughtfully undressed in the porch in order not to disturb his bride and, with his clothes and shoes tucked under his arm, climbed the winding staircase, only to discover that he was on top of a 14 bus.

'And I was quite wrong to suggest that people wouldn't object to jokes, since Dempster sued me instantly and won. My point, however, is that in those days one exercised discretion, yet now if the price is right we'll stitch up anyone. We should hang our heads in shame.'

'Bollocks,' my beloved said.

'You're right,' I said.

'I'm quite comfortable with what I do,' she said. 'How an eminent person behaves in private is taken by his biographer – once he's dead – to be of the utmost relevance. How much more important, surely, that we should know what he's up to while he's still in office.

'It's nonsense for Mrs Thatcher to say, as she did in the Commons recently, that a person's private life has no bearing on his public conduct, since if that was so he'd not feel obliged to resign instantly when caught.'

I wanted to ask Miss Laming to marry me, but I kept my head.

'The King of Spain,' I said, 'who, as you may have heard, is bailed to appear at Ealing on a deception charge – he had all his accounts sent to Buckingham Palace with an instruction that the Queen would settle them – is now living with me. Would you like to meet him?'

My beloved said yes, she would, suggesting that she'd come round to my flat later in the day. Since I had no further interest now in Tony the Drug Fiend, or in anything else, come to that, I excused myself at this point and returned home in a haze of love, where I found the King watching television in his little slippers.

'Buzz off,' I said.

'All right,' he said.

So far so good. A little light housework and then I bathed (since you never know, although you do), put out my Charlie Allen suit, prepared the soundtrack (seventies classics, black for the most part) and changed the lightbulbs from orange to a deceitful red since one prefers others these days to see only certain aspects of oneself indoors. And then D.C. Dick came head first through my front door with a couple of colleagues.

'D.C. Dick,' he said. 'Are you the King of Spain?'

'No,' I said. 'I told the King to buzz off.'

'Well get him back. Twelve other offences have come to light. My colleagues and I will return in an hour.'

'Look here, Mr Dick,' I said. 'I'm expecting a *News of the World* reporter with whom I've recently fallen in love. I don't want you running through my door within minutes of her arrival. That's not the stuff which impresses the *News of the World*.'

'Of course not,' said Mr Dick. 'I'll make myself scarce if I have your word that you'll take the King to court in the morning.'

That was decent of him, but my beloved didn't show, which baffles me, I must admit. I was definitely her type, I'm sure of that – a chap can tell. Now I've heard she's in the Canary Islands, if you please, and I'd like to know who with. The minx is playing with my feelings and she'll not get away with it. Sneaks and Co. will have to mount a full investigation.

69

My Beloved has an Early Night

Its all over between me and Sandie Laming. We were ships that passed in the night – which isn't to deny my feelings or suggest that she is anything less than perfect. It was the real thing all right – indeed, I cannot pass the wine bar where I saw her for the first and only time without a stab of pain, a sharp reminder that she possessed all the attributes of the ideal woman: a bruising indifference, an absent-minded unconcern, a promise in the proud tilt of her magnificent head that if you were cold and afraid and needed her she'd be thrillingly occupied elsewhere. You'd not come home, I judge, to find my ex-beloved at the ironing board or, dressed in something unbecoming, sewing buttons on your shirts.

What, then, caused everything to change? The realization, frankly, that not only does my literary agent, Alison, possess these attributes in abundance too, (I have described here, I think, the time when, at Bibendum, I fainted at the sight of her and came round to find that she'd taken this opportunity to have an early night) but also that I love her – deeply, unconditionally – as some people, I gather, love their children.

I discovered I loved her when, on the very day that I met my ex-beloved, Alison's team, the Los Angeles Raiders, stuffed mine, the Miami Dolphins, affording me nothing but joy and relief. If *wanting* your team to get stuffed isn't real love I don't know what is. And I'll go further: I wouldn't honestly give two hoots if my ex-beloved's team got stuffed, am uncertain if she even *has* a team, doubt, frankly, if she knows a wide receiver from a hole in the road. No – I was momentarily bewitched, that's all; I love my literary agent, Alison, and I knew this instantly when, grinning triumphantly, she joined me for dinner on the day the LA Raiders flattened the Miami Dolphins.

'My team beat your team!' she sang, wriggling with happiness in her chair. 'Ha! Ha! Ha! Golly, did we kick arse out there! Sammy Smith? Call him a running back? Dan Marino? What a tosser!'

I felt weak with love, thought I might faint again as I had before. 'You can't blame Dan Marino,' I said. 'Where was his pass protection?'

'Face down in the mud,' said Alison. 'They're big girls' blouses, your offensive line. How about Bo Jackson though? Rushing for 187 yards, including sixty-nine on a punt return. *That's* a running back.'

'As it happens,' I said, 'I rather prefer Marcus Allen.'

'Phooey!' she said. 'Marcus will get you a certain amount of first-down yardage, but for the big play give me Bo. And where was your defence? When the free safety spends the afternoon tackling running backs, the linebackers aren't doing their job.'

I realized of course that Sandie Laming – brilliant though she is – could never have lived at this conversational level, could never intellectually please a man such as myself, a typical Wykehamist who thrills only to the satisfactory thud of fat men running into each other at fifty miles per hour. I realized, too, that I was on a hiding to nothing here, so I changed the conversation.

'Did you see the New York Giants against the Eagles?'

'I certainly did,' said Alison. 'What a mess! Lawrence Taylor's lost a yard of pace. He didn't get a hand on Randall Cunningham all afternoon. Mind you – apart from Randall, the Eagles weren't so clever. What's up with Reggie White? Is he crook?'

'He's the best defensive end in the NFL,' I said.

'Not anymore. Dexter Manley's been reinstated.'

'At least Reggie White isn't required to live in a rehabilitation centre.'

'Maybe not,' said Alison. 'But he's got his bed booked in an old folks' home.'

And at this point I wondered whether the love I now felt for Alison was incompatible with my former feelings of perilous excitement, whether she had, like Lawrence Taylor, lost a yard of pace. She had recently shown small signs of caring – nothing as plonking as cooking duck *au poivre* or sewing curtains – but dispiriting little indications of loyalty and compassion for all that.

'Say something perfect,' I said. 'Cause my cerebral circuits to fuse.'

Alison thought for a moment and then excelled herself. 'I'm off to New York tomorrow with my American,' she said. 'With all the excitement ahead, I think I'll have an early night.'

I struggled home in a daze of love and, at 9.30, Sandie Laming rang. 'I can't chat,' she said. 'I'm off to Phoenix in the morning to interview Dexter Manley. You won't have heard of him, I don't suppose. He's the best defensive end in the NFL and recently joined the Cardinals after breaking the all-time sacking record with the Washington Redskins. And I hope to see my team, the New York Giants, stuff the overrated 49ers. It's just a question of breaking Joe Montana's rhythm. Ronnie Lott's worn out after ten years doing the linebackers' job and as for Roger Craig – my grandma could give him a five-yard start and catch him. Still, I mustn't bore you.'

Now I don't know where I am.

Ian Hislop and Les Negresses Vertes

It is a tribute to the genius of today's pop establishment that it can take a handful of ropey old Cole Porter songs, with their vulgar tunes and whingeing lyrics, and make them acceptable to a contemporary ear. Such, anyway, was the conclusion that I and a few of my young friends reached at a small party I gave on Saturday to view Channel 4's *Red Hot and Blue*.

Just before the kick-off Terence Blacker got an argument going by claiming that he'd seen a clip and that the high point of the show was a version of 'From This Moment On' by Mr Ian Hislop, backed by two naked men locked in a series of ballet moves. If this was so, I said, it seemed to exemplify the very English enthusiasm (though not Scottish, Welsh or Irish, as my colleague, Mr Alan Watkins, the distinguished rugby correspondent, was quick to point out) for the public display of day-dreams more gracefully acted out in the forgiving theatre of the mind.

'Don't have a go at me,' said Terence Blacker who, dressed in boots and a cowboy blouse, has been known to sing 'Don't Fence Me In' to his own accompaniment in a pizza bar and who assumed my remark was aimed at him.

I calmed him down by saying that he was one of the few

people I knew multi-talented enough to appear in public in different hats – in his case, either as the author of the brilliant comic novel *Fixx* or as the after-dark interpreter of Cole Porter's entire disgusting canon – and, thinking quickly on my feet, I explained that in fact I'd had in mind television programmes such as *Superstars*, in which sportsmen competed fatuously against each other in every discipline except the one in which they excelled. Thus we had been treated to the absurd sight of, say, a tubby little golfer playing ping-pong against the great Graham Price (the finest tighthead prop ever to pull on a Lions shirt, I said, though in my circle at least – and saving Mr Watkins's presence – argument still raged as to whether Pricey did or didn't collapse the scrum).

'He didn't,' said Mr Watkins.

'I'm not so sure,' said my best friend, Little Jo. 'I recall an occasion at Cardiff Arms Park . . .'

'A cauldron of emotion,' said my friend Wallace Arnold.

'That's as may be,' said Little Jo. 'My point is that on an English put-in on the Welsh five-yard line, Pricey speared Fran Cotton head first into the ground as if drilling for oil.'

Before Mr Watkins could answer this charge, Wallace Arnold said there was nothing more agreeable in his opinion than civilized speculation as to which English novelist might be the most accomplished cook of *pommes Lyonnaise*, which English cricketer might best turn a felicitous ode to Dame Fortune, or – to take up Mr Watkins's current ruminations at the back of the *Independent* – whether a team of Rugby League players would beat a selection accustomed to the Union code.

'The game would be over after the first scrummage,' said my literary agent, Alison. 'The league front row – unused to the mechanics of a Union scrum – would be stretchered off with broken backs. It would be more interesting to put up a team of American footballers against the All Blacks. Imagine an All Black scrum – the players as usual wearing white lace body-stockings under their kits – competing against Lawrence Taylor, Howie Long and Reggie White. Or picture a little All Black centre trying to stop half a hundred weight of running back coming at him at 30 m.p.h. After two weeks' coaching, the All Blacks would be well stuffed.'

'Fiddlesticks,' said Mr Watkins. 'There aren't enough hours in a day to teach an American footballer that he can only tackle the man with the ball.'

'As it happens,' said Little Jo, 'blocking is by no means unknown in Rugby Union. John Frame, a raw-boned Scottish centre, customarily ran full-tilt into his opposite number regardless of where the ball was. And how about W.P.C. Davies, an English centre built like a bollard? On a Lions tour of South Africa, Davies became restless because his partner on the wing, the great Tony O'Reilly, was marked by an unusually small Springbok. After twenty minutes, Davies approached O'Reilly and said: "I think I'll have a little run at your fellow if you don't mind, Reilly." O'Reilly agreed and, whenever Davies had the ball thereafter, he ran straight into the little Springbok, ironing him out like a pancake. O'Reilly spent the afternoon recovering the ball from the debris and strolling over the line for a record number of tries.'

At this point it was time to tune into *Red Hot and Blue* in which, as I expected, Cole Porter's rotten old cocktail songs were miraculously revitalized and in which – more unexpectedly, since I had not believed Terence Blacker on the score of Mr Ian Hislop's participation – the editor of *Private Eye* sang 'From This Moment On' in a charming falsetto, losing nothing by comparison with such gifted artists as Mr Iggy Pop, Miss Sinead O'Connor, The Pogues and Les Negresses Vertes.

Off the Pace, and a Bore to Boot

As I've grown older I've become a little unset in my ways. This is normal, I imagine. It's all over, more or less, and luckily there isn't time to put things right; small victories have been fortuitous, one's better schemes have ended in bizarre confusion; one has comforted those who wished one ill and frightened the life out of the few people one wanted to protect; nothing's at stake, nothing matters any more – so one can afford to experiment, to live more dangerously than one would have thought prudent hitherto.

This attitude, alas, tends to alarm young people who, keen to be adequately insured and pensioned, strive to make sensible arrangements, quite unaware, it seems, that soon enough it will all go wrong.

Not wishing to irritate anyone, and believing that after a certain age it is unbecoming to be pert or jaunty on the page, I decided, when I was invited to do this column, to keep under wraps this rather feckless aspect of myself – to be sternly unprovocative in fact. Judging that no one wants to be unsettled on a Saturday I have performed at a portly military medium – after the manner of those fat men called Cartwright who used to bowl for Warwickshire – seldom coming in at an unexpected angle or putting too much spin on the ball.

I trundled along quite happily until I spotted something odd: that whereas other columnists often kicked off by acknowledging their indebtedness to Mr So-and-So for pointing out that such-and-such was a better way of growing rhubarb, I was indebted to no one since I hadn't heard a dicky bird from the day I started here.

In my desire not to cause offence was I being a little *too* bland? When showing off for a living one prefers it if one's efforts aren't entirely disregarded, so I set off a squib or two, and then a larger one (a positive rocket, I thought) suggesting that one shouldn't take drugs in front of one's children since this would encourage them – contrary creatures that they are – to experiment with the alcohol culture, to say silly sweaty things in pubs, to tell jokes and vomit thereafter on the bathroom carpet.

When this advice failed to elicit a murmur of protest even from Essex, I went further, suggesting, more or less, that crack is good for you, that no one I know who takes it is as dependent on the stuff as half the Lords of Appeal are on a glass of whisky last thing at night, and agreeing with my friend Dr John Marks that hard drugs are dangerous because they're prohibited, not prohibited because they're dangerous.

That would do the trick, I thought. Never mind rhubarb, *that* would cause outraged ordinary mothers to write to me by the sackful – but not a bit of it. The only letter I received was from Dr Marks himself, who courteously pointed out that I had been most naïve to think my argument would cause an uproar since everyone agreed with it.

So there you are. Far from being a provocative old scallywag, I am laboriously in step, albeit a pace behind – taking up positions vacated a year before by Colchester and Chingford.

And I'm a bore to boot, which isn't quite the same since the ability to bore is a matter of style rather than content, an awesome intensity of purpose, a determination not so much to win an argument – which is reasonable enough – as to grind away at a subject which is of no interest to anyone except oneself. I've always been able to bore women, of course – I have admitted here already, I think, that I can make my best friend Little Jo literally weep with boredom – but more recently I've discovered that I can bore men too, can cause them to behave in this respect like women. When I was in Ibiza with Simon Carr – and a more *manly* man you couldn't hope to meet – he put up with me for a week or two and then one night, and near to tears, he suddenly stamped his foot and cried: 'Why must you go on and on? Why don't you take me out any more? Can't we just for once do something a little mad? I want to put on my prettiest clothes and go out dancing. I do! I do!'

More recently, when researching my television series, *Henry Root Into Europe*, I decided while driving from Hamburg to Baden-Baden to educate the three girls – Mark Chapman, Jeremy Lovering and Justin Judd – in the mysteries of American football. I only had a day and a half at my disposal but, even so, I might have made good progress had not Justin Judd fallen asleep at the wheel near Frankfurt and driven us into a ditch.

I've learnt my lesson, however. If one's own ideas are so humdrum that they cause others to burst into tears or fall asleep, the obvious remedy is to say the very opposite of what one thinks.

Last week, I took advantage of Ian Hislop's participation in *Red Hot and Blue* to say that Cole Porter wrote vulgar tunes and whingeing, illiterate lyrics.

What, I calculated, could be more provocatively absurd than that? As it happens, I haven't received a single outraged letter and now I don't know where I am. Next week I'll try rhubarb, I think.

Dunning My Friend Lord Weidenfeld

Keen as ever to be a whole hearted participant in the crass commercialization of Christmas, I spent an enjoyable few days in the run-up to the holiday planning how best to separate my friend Lord Weidenfeld from – as I saw it – moneys due to me.

Disappointed to have discovered that he'd settled a libel action on my behalf – thereafter, and without so much as a by-my-leave, paying damages from my share of accumulated proceeds – I intended to send him either a writ as a Christmas card (with his office closed, there'd be no one there to enter a defence, I thought, allowing me to obtain judgement by default and, pitching up on his premises in the New Year, to seize by way of settlement his swivel chairs and, perhaps, some *objets d'art*) or, in the first place – since it has always seemed to me dishonourable to instruct solicitors when pursuing a personal vendetta – a startlingly ill-mannered letter.

I was in the middle of composing this ('While your needs are greater than mine, no doubt . . .' – that sort of stuff) when, during a coffee break, I turned to the *Daily Telegraph* for moral inspiration. While not expecting to find anything here about the rights and wrongs of hustling Lord Weidenfeld, I had hoped that the small thoughtful essay on the meaning of Christmas would have been done this year by Geoffrey Wheatcroft, but discovered that, on this occasion, he'd turned in the one about the puritanism of the drink/driving regulations – 'Humbug over Death on the Roads' – leaving the other one – 'True Light behind the Empty Hype' – to Christopher Booker.

Mr Wheatcroft was in rather subdued form, I thought, arguing, unprovocatively enough, that the right of social inadequates to stuply themselves with alcohol and smash each other to bits in agreeable country lanes ('There is little point in driving several miles to nurse a gin and tonic') should not be inhibited by a plod with a breathalyser bag, later suggesting that police powers in this respect were on all fours with interning carriers of the HIV virus.

Mr Booker's essay, on the other hand, caused me to sit up

straight and re-examine some deeply held beliefs – an uncomfortable but salutary exercise at any time of year. The meaning of Christmas, Mr Booker argued, was not to be found in the dreadful corporate yuletide, the Muzak in packed supermarkets pouring out the syrup of carol music, the false bonhomie and sentimentality on television. This hadn't occurred to me, I must admit. As someone who likes Muzak (though preferring a *Price is Right* 'Easy on the Ear' selection to spooky old carols), who had hitherto thought it no bad thing that, once a year, atheists should be intimidated into buying one another presents, putting on paper hats and playing charades with people they disliked, even watching Maureen Lipman in a televised snowball fight with spastics, I hurried on through Mr Booker's essay, keen to discover the real purpose behind this strange event.

It was, Mr Booker explained, a religious festival, a time when we should escape from our ego-selves, which can only see the world through the tunnel vision of egotism, into our other deeper selves which connect us to the world outside ourselves and make us feel joyfully alive.

Eager to connect, I instantly abandoned my plans to watch *Dirty Dancing* with the pussycats and rang up Jillypoo.

'What the hell do you want?' she said. 'Don't you know it's Christmas?'

'I do indeed,' I said. 'I've been reading the *Daily Telegraph* which says that you and I are locked into our ego-selves.'

'Here,' said Jillypoo. 'That's well out of order.'

'It doesn't mention you and me personally,' I said. 'However, we should get out and about more. I had thought of hopping over to Romania but discovered, also from the *Daily Telegraph*, that Lord Deedes is already doing that one. No point in two old gents poking about and reporting back. It might depress them.'

'Are you taking the piss or what?'

'Certainly not. Perhaps we could visit the poor.'

Jillypoo's snort of derision could have blown the pair of us to cardboard city. 'They should visit us,' she said.

'We could talk to them,' I said. 'Explain – as I've also read in the *Telegraph* – that conversation is the highest human ideal.'

'Look,' said Jillypoo. 'Me, I'm sat here drawing up a list of all the people who owe me money. So bugger off out of it, will you?'

'Good at collecting debts, are you?'

'I get them eventually. I've just done my mother. It took me twenty years, but I got her in the end.'

This gave me an idea. If her own mother was no match for Jillypoo, Lord Weidenfeld would be a piece of cake. I gave her his address and she will be visiting him in the New Year. I wouldn't be in his boots for all the tea in China and, with this happy seasonal thought, I sat back and switched on *Dirty Dancing*.

Mr Lott and Tina Brown

Some of our gossip columnists have attempted irony, I am afraid, following my friend Tina Brown's decision to cancel the party she planned to give for the launch in this country of *Vanity Fair*.

'It seems to me obvious,' one of them wrote last week, 'that – given the importance which *Vanity Fair*, by pompously cancelling it, has shown it attaches to its party – the appropriate thing would have been for George Bush and Saddam Hussein to postpone their war until after the party had been held.'

This is most unjust. Miss Brown may not thank me for making public the actual reason for the cancellation, but I feel in all fairness that I must. Telephoning me from New York two weeks ago, she said she had suddenly become nauseated at the prospect of all those media inadequates getting drunk at her expense and decided, instead, to arrange a more intimate reunion with a handful of her real friends. Would I, she said, like to attend a small gathering at Blakes Hotel on Sunday 27 January?

'And please don't mention this in your column,' she added. 'A lot of people might wonder why I hadn't asked them.'

And it was only later that I realized Tina's get-together clashed with the celebrated kedgeree and Superbowl party that I and my literary agent, Alison, give in January each year. Here was a problem. I didn't want to let Tina down (not least because I hoped – following an informal inquiry she made some weeks ago – to be engaged as *Vanity Fair's* style and interiors correspondent) but nor did I wish to disappoint my literary agent, Alison, or, come to that, all those people for whom our Superbowl party is the highlight of their social year.

I was wondering how to resolve this difficulty when – complication upon complication – Ronnie Lott, the 49ers free safety and unarguably the finest defensive player ever to grace American football, telephoned me from San Francisco to see if I'd like to be his guest at Superbowl XXV in Tampa, Florida. As readers of this column will know, I love my literary agent, Alison, with a deliquescing intensity more usually associated with fainting teenyboppers. But I have never denied to her, or indeed to anyone else, that I am in love, too, with Mr Lott (the upshot, I dare say, of my Winchester education and a condition from which I might have been spared, perhaps, had Esther Rantzen's hot-line been available to public schoolboys thirty years ago). I had never imagined that I might have to choose between them. I decided to confront Alison face to face.

'I have a problem,' I said. 'Ronnie Lott has invited me to watch Superbowl XXV from his private box in Tampa. It's the chance of a lifetime, of course, but I don't want to go without you. What shall I do?'

She solved the problem instantly. 'Don't worry,' she said, 'I quite understand. You mustn't disappoint Ronnie Lott, so I'll go to Tampa and you can stay here.'

That made sense, so I rang Mr Lott in San Francisco and said that, heartbreaking though it was to me, my literary agent, Alison, had decided to accept his invitation in my place – whereon Mr Lott, marvellous man that he is, said he could find room in his box for another person so that we both could go.

'Terrific news,' I said to Alison. 'Ronnie Lott can get another ticket.'

Alison frowned. 'I don't know,' she said. 'I am not sure if there's anyone I'd like to take.'

'What about me?' I said.

She looked quite startled. 'I suppose so. All right, then.'

It was nice to go to America again, to be reminded how much more civilized they are than us, how wise and ironic, and much too courteous to sneer at us for our attitude to them – insulting them behind their backs but adopting a doggy posture in their presence – but the match itself was rather spoilt for me (and for

Ronnie Lott, too, I think) by Alison's ability to read a game, to tell us what would happen some time before it did.

'The Giants,' she said, 'are playing a two-down-line to spoil the Bills' passing game. The Bills will expect to blow the Giants' linebackers away opening huge holes for Thurman Thomas, but it won't work. If it's down to the last drive, Jim Kelly, the Bills' overrated quarterback won't get to within Norwood's kicking distance on grass and that will be that.'

And so it was. After the game I told Alison we must return home immediately since I'd promised Tina Brown that, having missed her party, I'd have lunch with her on Tuesday. I was keen, I said, to become *Vanity Fair's* style and interiors correspondent.

'In fact,' Alison said, 'we are going to New York for the Giants' celebration party. You can wait for me at the hotel. And don't worry about Tina. I told her that the terms of your contract with the *Independent* wouldn't allow you to work for her, so she's given me the job.'

I am filing this from the Algonquin and hope to return next week.

Addressed by the Auk at a Tender Age

Would you want your boy to turn out like Stormin' Norman or like Emma Thompson – a real man, that is to say, or a chap with a sense of humour, prepared to put on a red nose for Comic Relief and participate, unencouraged, in a skit?

Stormin' Norman, obviously – that's the desired end – but what should be the means? More precisely, is it to be Winchester or Eton? One or the other, clearly, but at which is he less likely to fall victim to a time-honoured atrocity involving knotted tea-towels – thereafter, and as a matter of self-defence – acquiring a range of funny faces?

This question didn't concern me too much, I admit, when it was time to educate my boy, Charlie, but a vague determination that he shouldn't have the same advantages in life that I'd enjoyed persuaded me in the end to send him to Eton rather than to Winchester.

That's not true, in fact. I didn't send him anywhere. My wife sent him to Eton and I was as surprised as you'd have been when she turned up at my place one evening and told me that that was where he was, adding that, in her opinion, he was off the rails and needed a father's influence.

To be obliging I hopped down to Eton the next day and took the wrong lad out to lunch, later persuading him – since I didn't like the look of the place – to return with me to London. When, after a month or two, he told me that he wasn't mine but Gay Kindersley's boy, Kim, I sent him packing, and now he's an actor, if you please, which must be a worry to Gay.

On the other hand, and with regard to a sense of humour, my boy Charlie and I have turned out well, neither of us having one. We are more likely, in fact, through the sudden application of a headlock on a doe-eyed junior half our size, to have been the cause of one in others.

As between Winchester and Eton I concluded many years ago that it's six of one and half a dozen of the other, with Winchester enjoying a slight edge, perhaps, since I've remained on the straight and narrow, more or less, whereas my boy Charlie did for a while join the alcohol culture, being funny in pubs with his zip undone. He's all right now, however.

I wouldn't have given the matter further thought but, in the past year, many of my friends have consulted me with regard to schools and, as a consequence, I've sent Michael O'Mara's boy, aged four, to Eton, Jillypoo's son to Winchester and regretfully told Pratley that, since his Giles is a no-hoper anyway, he might as well go to Stowe, Charterhouse or even Shrewsbury.

More recently my best friend, Susan Carr, roped me in to advise on her boy Alexander's education, rightly judging that I'd be a more reliable guide in this respect than her husband, Simon, who has just completed the funniest novel ever written (*The Hop Quad Dolly*, to be published in June) and is, as a consequence, a little bushed right now.

On Saturday, Susan and I and Alexander drove down to Winchester and I was able, as I showed them round the school, to lay to rest many of the slanders uttered against it down the years, not least that it turns out eggheads.

'In fact,' I said, 'prowess at games was everything. Luckily, I shone in this regard, since my mother engaged top professionals to coach me in the holidays — Sir Stanley Matthews at football and George Geary at cricket. They took their meals with the servants and were paid 7s 6d a week. Not a lot of money even in those days. This is War Cloisters, by the way, where, on a misty March day, Field Marshal Wavell once addressed the school. A bit suspect Wavell, I've always thought. *Other Men's Flowers*. Into battle with an anthology in his pocket. That can't be right. Small wonder he was replaced in the desert by the Auk. The Auk also addressed the school and, if you've been addressed by the Auk at an impressionable age, you measure up thereafter, I can tell you. Mind that boy. I think he's still alive.'

'My God,' said Susan, stepping over the body of a small boy lying on the pavement. 'What's happened to him?'

'Probably the victim of a bross blow,' I said. 'When I was here an older boy, thinking he'd been cheeked, could line you up and pot you in the stomach. With a well-aimed strike below the heart, an accomplished thug could knock you cold for thirty seconds. Those were the days. On my first night, returning to the dormitory after prayers, I found that some of the older boys had torn the head off my panda. Another boy, risking the bullies' fury, borrowed a needle and cotton from matron and sewed it on again.'

'How courageous of him,' Susan said. 'How did you thank him?'

'I hit him,' I said, 'causing him to acquire a sense of humour on the spot. Later, the bullies and I destroyed his model theatre. He's a playwright now. I blame myself. Where are you going?'

'Back to London,' said Susan. 'I want to discover where Emma Thompson went to school.'

Some people you can't help. And now I've discovered that Michael O'Mara's boy, aged four, has run away from Eton and is suing his father for cruel and unusual treatment. Comic Relief is here to stay, I fear.

A Good Restaurant Not to Go to the Theatre From

I must apologise to the many ferry passengers who got stuck in the Channel on Monday evening. The two-hour delay was caused by Mark Chapman, the gifted director of my television series, *Root Into Europe*, who, at a problematic moment, took charge of the ship's smart technology and – like air traffic control coaching an amateur in how to land a stricken plane – talked Jane, his beloved, through a recipe for spaghetti bolognese.

We'd set off that morning for a day's research at sea (up on the bridge – 'at ease, don't mind us') and I had everything pretty much under control ('that bollard will have to go') until a sudden force nine wind caused a traffic jam outside Dover. The captain would have negotiated this successfully, I think, had I not asked Chapman what he was having for dinner that night.

'Spaghetti bol . . . my God!' he said. 'I won't be home in time to do the sauce! Mind out, captain. I've got to speak to my beloved.' Twenty minutes later the captain, who had been unable to communicate with Dover while Chapman spoke urgently to Jane, was obliged to tell his other punters that we were now at the back of the queue and would be entering harbour two hours late.

At this point Chapman and I left the bridge and joined the other passengers – the latter being mere specimens to us, of course, to be eyed with an unforgiving, documentary-maker's gaze.

'With hand-held camera and skilful post-production work, we could hold this lot up to peak-time ridicule,' I said. 'It must be awful to be a member of the general public.'

'Nothing worse,' said Chapman. 'Mind you, they seem quite cheerful in spite of the delay. Perhaps they've all got tickets for *Les Misérables* tonight and have suddenly realized they won't have to see it after all. Every cloud, etcetera.'

This reminded me of a conversation I'd had with Stephen Pile when I was the *Tatler*'s award-winning restaurant critic. Since it didn't occur to me that anyone would want to read about someone else's lunch, I used to take interesting people to the restaurant of their choice and thereafter write about them instead of the food. When it was Pile's turn, he chose a pizza-parlour in Shaftesbury Avenue that was pretty disgusting even by my standards. I asked him why he had brought us to such a place.

'It's a very good restaurant not to go to the theatre from,' he said.

Not going to the theatre is one of life's enduring pleasures, of course, but Pile took unusual steps to obtain maximum gratification. Any fool, he pointed out, could sit at home in a state of not being at the theatre. He preferred to buy tickets, trudge up West, eat a meal in a mood of pained anticipation and then – glorious release – decide to skip the play.

'From this very restaurant,' he said, 'I've not been to more civilized comedies than you've had hot lunches.'

I saw the sense of it, but even so I wasn't entirely satisfied. Surely one could not go to the theatre from any number of restaurants. What, I asked, was so special about this one?

'Ah,' said Pile, with the apologetic air of a man who has not made himself entirely clear. 'You're forgetting something. I'm from the West Country, aren't I?'

I never did manage to work this out, but I now told Chapman that Stephen Pile would have preferred not to see *Les Misérables* from a pizza-parlour in Shaftesbury Avenue.

'That's as may be,' said Chapman. 'Since we've time to kill, however, I'd like to pick your brains about a new development of mine. We're planning a documentary about people who've disappeared, but we can't find anyone suitable.'

I was astonished. 'Of course you can't find anyone suitable,' I said. 'They've all disappeared.'

It was Chapman's turn to look surprised. 'Damn me, you're right,' he said. 'Back to square one.'

No one likes to see a development go down the drain, so I suggested that a lot of the people who've disappeared might secretly be writing scripts for *Whose Line is It Anyway?* This seemed to annoy Chapman who must have shares, I think, in this silly, self-regarding little show.

'It isn't scripted,' he said.

'Of course it is,' I said. 'A child of three could see it's been rehearsed. The mystery is why – this being so – it's quite so feeble.'

'It isn't feeble,' said Chapman, 'and I shall now return to the bridge to discover whether Jane, my beloved, has followed my instructions with regard to the bolognese.'

When he returned, he was looking angrier than before.

'The sauce is down the drain?' I said.

'Even worse,' said Chapman. 'She's booked seats on Friday for *Les Misérables*. What's the name of Pile's restaurant?'

'I can't remember.'

'She's got a ticket for you, too.'

'The Pizza on a Plate,' I said. 'See you there at seven o'clock.'

Tony the Drug Fiend and Kensington Palace

When my friend Tony the Drug Fiend got potted in 1985 the arresting officer – an unusually conscientious detective sergeant – played back all the messages on his answering machine and then hurried to Kensinton Palace with a search warrant and some awkward questions. Here he was potted, himself, by the police guarding the place. He is now directing traffic in Hong Kong.

I don't want to visit Hong Kong myself, so when Mary Kenny suggested recently in the *Sunday Telegraph* that thoughtful people should spend less time disparaging our judicial system and more offering help and sympathy to those who have suffered at the hands of vicious criminals, I decided when following her advice, to skip Kensington Palace and to check out instead the welfare of Tony the Drug Fiend's other victims, not least myself.

I'm not doing too well, as it happens, and Tony the Drug Fiend is undoubtedly to blame. While he was doing his six years in Maidstone he acquired fifteen A levels and degrees in economics and astrophysics. It is not necessary to go along with the *Sunday Telegraph*'s line (that higher education is a dangerous handicap in the real world) if I say that, for all the good his new

86

qualifications have been to me, he might just as well have stayed inside.

Nor, I think, is it to agree wholeheartedly with the incomparable Geoffrey Wheatcroft – who argued this week in the *Sunday Telegraph* that 'most of us would rather be governed by two dozen chaps picked at random from the public bar than by the assembled fellows of All Souls' (most of us, I imagine, would prefer it in fact if anyone entering a public bar were disenfranchised on the spot, not least representatives of the delirium tremens school of columnists) – if I admit that a street-smart lad from the wrong end of the Fulham Road is more likely than a fellow of All Souls to connect you to the national grid in such a way as to ensure that the electricity board imburse you quarterly rather than vice versa, or to fit you out with a pair of Armani trousers for £6.50 or an untraceable BMW and a range of alternative documents, such as a realistic passport, a driving licence and a MOT certificate. For all such services, I and his other lamentably over-educated clients – a professor at the London School of Economics, a distinguished American novelist, the editor of an influential broadsheet – relied on Tony the Drug Fiend.

It's all about whether you're an ivory tower twit, isn't it, or a real man with common sense leaking out of his ears like Tony the Drug Fiend or a contributor to the *Sunday Telegraph*? Speaking for myself, I'm not ashamed to admit that, if in the old days there was a man's job to be done in the house (a socket to be changed, an over flow in the servant's quarters to be plugged) or, more dangerously, a ruffian at the front door to be dispatched, I'd first turn to my wife and then, if her toolbox was not up to the job or if the ruffian was too persistent, to Tony the Drug Fiend.

He had 'contacts'. I don't have contacts, never have had, wouldn't know a contact if I fell underneath one, but whatever you wanted – or didn't want, come to that – Tony the Drug Fiend always had a contact, often in north London, who could deliver it to your front door, carriage paid, in two-and-a-half hours. Never mind what fell off the back of a lorry, Tony the Drug Fiend could get you the lorry too. He could get you a staircase, not that I ever needed one. All the more disastrous, then that within weeks of his getting potted, my wife left me for artistic reasons, taking her toolbox with her: a double blow that has caused me and my immediate environment slowly to disintegrate. I don't know about Kensington Palace, but judging by my electricity bills I'm paying for the Blackpool illuminations, and my trousers, frankly, are a disgrace. In the circumstances, it's not surprising that I kicked my heels impatiently while Tony the Drug Fiend served his sentence – could hardly wait, indeed, for the day of his release, for his rewiring my premises to my advantage and for a new pair of Armani trousers.

Forget it. His trousers are worse than mine, his head is so bulging with abstract speculation that he can hardly cross the street unaided and on the day he got out he asked *me* if I could get *him* a staircase. Worst of all, he can no longer understand a simple telephonic code. On Tuesday I rang him and ordered a pound of cooking chocolate. Two hours later a pound of cooking chocolate was precisely what I got.

It was time, I thought, to discover whether his other victims were doing any better. The distinguished American novelist asked me to mend a hole in his bathroom ceiling, but I was laughing so much I couldn't help. His trousers! And when I pitched up at Kensington Palace I found them reading the *Sunday Telegraph*.

'Education?' they said. 'Forget it. Judging by our electricity bills, we're wired up to Harrods.'

'Why are you packing?' I said.

'We're leaving for Hong Kong tomorrow,' they said.

Then they tried to sell me a pound of cooking chocolate.

Eve Pollard Buys my Lime-green Wedding Suit

I have received a rocket from Kensington Palace. They thought it was indiscreet of me to mention them here in connection with Tony the Drug Fiend. This surprised me. I take the view that if you think it's wrong to smoke the occasional substance you shouldn't do it – and I said as much to the starchy young equerry who rebuked me on the telephone.

'We're not bothered about that,' he said. 'We object to your suggestion that, prior to his being potted, we relied on him for discount trousers, passports and plumbing.'

'Well, didn't you?' I said.

'Certainly,' he said. 'And for all the good the degrees he acquired in prison have been to us he might as well have stayed inside. The place is falling apart, and – this is in confidence, you understand – it is shortly to be featured on *Through the Keyhole*. We hope to win the holiday for two in Majorca.'

I know how they feel. I had to borrow someone else's premises for my own appearance on *Through the Keyhole*, and when Mark Chapman, the gifted director of my television series, *Root Into Europe*, asked me to dinner on Thursday I turned him down because I had nothing to wear.

'Nor you have,' he said. 'But don't worry. I'll kit you out in something of mine. You can put it on when you get here.'

He then mentioned the lime-green wedding suit which I greatly admired, you may remember, when he wore it last summer at the marriage of Justin Judd and Emma Laybourne. On that occasion, indeed, I tried to buy it from him. He wanted £400 for it, so I offered him £600 cash on the table, and at that point negotiations broke down.

Be that as it may, we went straight to the wardrobe when I pitched up at his place on Thursday evening.

'Right,' he said. 'The lime gre . . . goats and monkeys! Someone's pinched my lime-green wedding suit!'

'Good heavens,' I said.

'Who'd do a thing like that?' he said.

I would, I suppose – indeed, I had. I'd borrowed it earlier in the week for my appearance on *Through the Keyhole* – a show I particularly wanted to do since I was as keen as the chaps at Kensington Palace to win the holiday for two in Majorca. It would be a nice break, I thought, for my literary agent, Alison.

I did have a problem, though. My own premises were quite unsuitable and I had some difficulty persuading friends to let me use theirs.

I first tried Jillypoo, but she told me that she was suing Wandsworth Council for subsidence. This surprised me since she seemed to be doing well. She's driving a Bentley and the boy's at Winchester.

'Do you mean subsistence?' I said.

'No,' she said. 'I mean subsidence. The house is sinking at the rate of three feet a year.'

That ruled her place out and I next tried Terence Blacker. His circumstances seemed ideal (an enchanting wife, two delightful children, a garden with a willow tree, two hens, a rabbit) but when I asked if I might borrow them he said he couldn't, as a serious novelist, allow his family and home to appear on television with David Frost and Wayne Sleep. That was rich, coming from a man who, to publicize his brilliant comic novel *Fixx* sang 'Don't Fence Me In' in public on a horse. But then I had a bit of luck. I discovered that Mark Chapman was in the Dordogne with Jane, his beloved, so I let myself into his house with the spare key he keeps in the office.

The place was perfect – not least because the celebrity panel on *Through the Keyhole* would never guess it was lived in by a man. The elegant kitchen, the display of gels and mousses in the bathroom and the designer clothes hanging in the wardrobe would suggest to anyone that the owner was a successful woman – Anouska Hempel, perhaps, or Linda Agran – Anita Roddick at a pinch. The holiday in Majorca was in the bag, I thought, and after Lloyd Grossman had filmed the place I pitched up at the studio confident that the guest celebrities would be utterly foxed. And so they were.

'It isn't Kensington Palace,' said Willie Rushton. 'And that's in its favour. Anouska Hempel, that's my guess.'

'A power dresser, certainly,' said Eve Pollard. 'But more a media type, perhaps. Linda Agran?'

'Anita Roddick,' said Wayne Sleep, 'without a doubt.'

I came on at this point and claimed my holiday for two in Majorca.

'There aren't any prizes,' said David Frost.

'Never mind,' said Eve Pollard. 'Your lime-green suit would look better on me. £600.'

I wasn't going to be caught by the same trick twice. '£400,' I said.

'Done,' she said.

I was pleased about that – less pleased by my literary agent Alison's reaction to my not winning the holiday for two in Majorca. To make it up to her, I bought us two tickets to Florida.

'I've booked a holiday for two in Florida,' I said.
'Good,' she said. 'I'll go by myself twice.'

In TV, We Put the Money on the Screen

I had not thought that either my literary agent, Alison, or Mark Chapman, the gifted director of my television series, *Root into Europe*, read this column, but both do, it seems, and neither is pleased by some of the things I said last week.

Mark Chapman wants me to recover his lime-green wedding suit – which I sold on screen for £400, you may remember, to Eve Pollard while recording *Through the Keyhole* (tune in at 7p.m. on 10 May) – and my literary agent, Alison, was not amused by my joke about our holiday for two in Florida. She would not be so selfish, she says, as to go by herself twice. She also wishes me to make it clear that, thanks to her, my apartment – which I suggested was not up to an appearance on *Through the Keyhole* – is not the tip it was.

There's not much I can do about the lime-green wedding suit. Miss Pollard wore it on Tuesday for Lady Edith Foxwell's party at the Embargo Club, and it looked better on her, I must admit, than it had on me – or on Chapman, come to that – but not as good as it did on Janet Street-Porter to whom she sold it for £600 in the course of the party.

I can, however, credit my literary agent, Alison, with having improved my flat. Last summer, you may remember, the *Observer* decided not to feature it in its excellent 'A Room of My Own' series on the grounds that it might depress their readers. This had hurt me at the time, I said, because my wife had just done it up – or rather, half done it up. Keen to fashion it in the manner of the breakfast room of a five-star Hamburg hotel, we'd replaced the bottle green curtains and carpets with stuff in dirty pink and Cambridge blue and bought a three-piece suite.

Unfortunately, we ordered the three-piece suite without first

91

measuring the room, with the result that the sofas and chairs were far too big. Visitors looked like midgets, their little legs dangling over the edge of the sofa as if they were participating in a surrealistic comedy by N.F. Simpson. My wife had then walked out, leaving me with a dirty pink carpet, bottle green curtains and a satirical three-piece suite.

It was then that my literary agent, Alison, decided to buff the place up. She was defeated by the three-piece suite, but by adding new curtains, lamps and cushions – dressing the set, as we'd have said in the theatre – she has made the place look very jolly. The problem has been that the flat belongs to my wife, further that she is not aware of Alison's existence. Since she might not like another woman doing up one of her properties I have, when receiving an hour's notice of an intended visit, quickly removed Alison's improvements and re-instated my wife's possessions (kept in the wings, so to speak, for such a contingency). This is quite a performance, I can tell you.

When I was a theatrical producer, I'd have requisitioned a revolve from one of my shows, installed it in the drawing-room and, with a flick of a switch, spun my wife's stuff on and Alison's off. Those were the days. I wasn't a particularly good producer, not because I was bad at business but because I had appalling taste.

Luckily, I'd learnt my craft from a fat entrepreneur of the old school. He never put on a show whose set wouldn't, at the end of an irrelevantly short run, look good in his drawing-room; for the sake of his wardrobe, the juvenile lead had to be as fat as he was; and the ingenue was always the same size as his mistress. Everything I knew I learnt from him; I once persuaded John Bird that his satirical review, *Here is the News*, would be best accompanied by a fifteen-piece strict tempo dance band placed on stage. When the show folded in Oxford I inherited fifteen sky-blue bandsmen's suits; as a consequence I spent the sixties looking like Geraldo and his orchestra – the reason, perhaps, that, having missed out the first time round, I'm now doing the sixties on my own.

In the circumstances, it's a keen disappointment that Mark Chapman, having hired me as associate producer on *Root Into Europe* seems unwilling to make use of my business acumen. On Thursday he was quite surprised when, at a wardrobe meeting, I suggested the leading man's suits should fit me rather than George Cole, and that we should cast an ingenue whose measurements were the same as Alison's.

'There isn't an ingenue,' said Chapman.

'That never bothered us in the old days,' I said.

'In television,' he said, 'we put the money on the screen. And don't forget we're going to Amsterdam next week.'

That wouldn't be possible, in fact (not that I told Chapman this), since I was off to Florida on Monday with Alison – who was still fretting about my holiday-for-two joke.

'Have you made it clear,' she said, 'that I wouldn't be so selfish as to go by myself twice?'

'Yes,' I said. 'I'm looking forward to it.'

'Why?' she said. 'Won't you miss me?'

'Why should I miss you?'

'Because I'll be going with one of my young friends.'

And I'll be filing this from Amsterdam.

A Little Loco on Location

Disappointed, perhaps, by the inability of his researchers to discover anyone who's disappeared, Mark Chapman – by disappearing himself – has made a significant contribution to his TV development, *Where are They Now?* He was last seen on Thursday at Amsterdam airport, singing 'We'll Meet Again' as he boarded a plane for Acapulco. More seriously, Jeremy Lovering has started a new life in Amsterdam's Bohemian quarter with a personal palliasse and a Primus stove.

Location-spotting for *Root Into Europe*, the three of us had earlier been driving round Amsterdam in search of a cannabis café in which Root – lost in the red-light district on his way to meet the chief of police – would seek directions, thereafter (and inadvertently) sampling the chocolate cake. It would be amusing, I said, if we ourselves became lost, even more amusing if we then sought directions in a cannabis café, subsequently making the same mistake as Root. A chap could all too easily get snarled up in his own research, I said. A playwright friend of mine had received a Bafta award and a two-year suspended sentence after he'd experimented with his agent's credit cards while researching a series on fraud.

'Don't be silly,' said Chapman. 'How could we get lost? And the reek of cannabis would alert us instantly.'

'Why, in that case, wouldn't it alert Root?' I said. 'We seem to be suggesting that a nice old English party can get stoned unwittingly in Amsterdam.'

'Now you're being negative,' said Chapman.

Then we got lost. This annoyed me because we, like Root, had an appointment with Amsterdam's chief of police – the awesomely civilized Commander Bob Visser – and I was keen to discover whether, since our successful meeting with him last year, he'd followed my advice with regard to Holland's drug policies, specifically whether he'd done anything about Amsterdam's crack problem (you couldn't get it, I'd said).

Lovering – a conscientious researcher in the normal run of things – also began to fret a bit since he urgently didn't want to miss a rendezvous in Paris with Candida, his beloved.

In the event, and having asked the way in several cannabis cafés, we were half an hour late for our appointment with Commander Visser. Bearing in mind Lovering's pressing other rendezvous, I decided to ignore Chapman's suggestion that the Commander should get the ball rolling and to bring him swiftly up to date instead with the latest state of affairs in England.

'It's madness,' I said. 'Except in Liverpool, where my friend Dr John Marks, by prescribing hard drugs to patients, has reduced drug-taking and acquisitive crime and brought about a startling improvement in addicts' health. For all that, the Association of Chief Police Officers recently decided that the war against drugs should be stepped up. The attitude of the British police must break your heart. Right – that's enough of that. Young Lovering's got a plane to catch.'

Encouraged by Chapman, the Commander politely pointed out that, while the Liverpool model was indeed impressive, Holland's own liberal policies seem to be working. Only 9 per cent of the carriers of the Aids virus were intravenous drug users, compared to 30 per cent in the rest of Europe. Drugs-related crime rates were very low compared with other European cities and the percentage of young drug users was decreasing fast. Only

4 per cent of Dutch addicts were under the age of twenty-one. Seven years ago, the figure had been 14 per cent.

'As for the British police,' the Commander said, 'I do find their attitude rather inconsistent. Their operational activities are often quite civilized, but they'd never admit to this in public. It seems to be a policy of "not in front of the children . . ." A very British attitude, if I may say so.'

At this point, Lovering and I managed to persuade Chapman it was time to leave, but on the way to the airport he suddenly stopped the car and dived into an elegant chocolate shop. Minutes later he emerged with several little boxes tastefully secured by pink ribbon.

'Presents for your beloveds,' he said.

'Better sample them,' said Lovering. He thoughtfully chewed a couple of chocolates and then climbed slowly out of the car. 'I'm off to start a new life in the Bohemian quarter,' he said.

'What about Candida, your beloved?' I said.

'I'm an artist,' he said, and he disappeared round a corner.

Shame really. Still – they come and they go. The moon's a balloon. Meanwhile, I advised Chapman not to sample the chocolates – advice he chose to ignore.

'Head like a rock,' he said.

I got him to the airport but there he boarded a plane for Acapulco, expressing much the same sentiments as Lovering had. Never mind. Justin Judd, the producer of *Root Into Europe*, and I have already begun the search for a new director – funded by the *Where are They Now?* development budget.

The Shirt Should Match the Eyes

Chapman, Lovering and I – still researching *Root Into Europe* – had by Wednesday moved our business temporarily to Paris where, al fresco with other artists on a boulevard (tea at Les Deux Magots, to be precise) I noticed that Chapman's socks had eleven different colours in them and, more tellingly, that each subtle interlocking shade blended perfectly with another aspect of his afternoon ensemble.

Such a discovery might in the normal run of things have brought me down, but I happened to be in excellent spirits, looked for once as good as Chapman, if not better (though not as good as Lovering), had, quite unusually, been complimented by a Frenchman on my trousers, indeed had been asked by Claude Terrail – the owner of La Tour d'Argent and five times winner of France's Best Dressed Man Award – who my tailor was.

Six hours earlier I had arrived in Paris to discover that my shirts, lingerie and half-hose were on their way to Dublin. To a naval man such as myself, this was neither here nor there, but Chapman ruled that he couldn't take me, looking like a ratbag, to La Tour d'Argent, where we were due to have lunch with Mr Terrail himself. Accordingly, he organized a two-hour shopping spree in the course of which I discovered not only how you get your clothes to fit you, more or less (prior to purchase you try them on: jackets, trousers – shirts even, if you please), but the secret, too, of the co-ordinated ensemble effect (you match stuff up, taking into account the colour of your eyes and so forth).

'According to Cary Grant,' Chapman said, 'the mistake most men make is to match their tie with their shirt. In fact, the tie should match the eyes.'

Be that as it may, I was complimented on my outfit at La Tour d'Argent, and now, legs stretched outside Les Deux Magots, I said how nice it must be for the other two to be abroad with an accommodating old party such as myself, with someone who never sulked or called the odds, who stood still even while another chap matched his eyes with haberdashery on offer.

'In fact,' said Chapman, 'you're impossible. If things go wrong you howl like a two-year-old and stamp your feet. Roll on October, when we'll be shot of you.'

Do what? I was astonished, frankly, fell into a deep silence while I thought the matter through. My occasional moods, surely, were symptoms merely of advancing age, but then it hit me that I'd always been a trifle temperamental, not least when in the navy. Whoever had deployed the 5th Submarine Squadron, based at Portsmouth, he, like Chapman, had refused to plan its day-to-day manoeuvres with my convenience in mind.

Just as Chapman's team – aiming to drive to Brussels, say, from Paris – always sets off at breakfast time, so also the 5th Submarine Squadron – ordered to participate in some damned-fool Nato exercise – always sailed at some ungodly hour, often 2a.m. As a consequence, our First Lieutenant, 'Bosun Grieg', was compelled to abandon his other duties and instead comfort and pacify one small, infuriated midshipman who was stamping his feet at the back of the bridge and threatening to tell his mother what a load of bollocks this whole silly operation was.

Chapman, equally, often has to put on hold his other pressing duties ('pan, fade, cut – take five, darlings') while he discovers why I have a face like thunder, whether I'm warm enough or want a glass of milk.

On the other hand, the 5th Submarine Squadron, having set sail in the middle of the night, seldom pitched up in the right place (aiming at Gibraltar once we surfaced – rather to our surprise, and to theirs, too, I expect – in a marine leisure complex in Copenhagen), whereas Chapman's party, aiming at Paris, often makes it – albeit with one's lingerie in Dublin.

This week, however, he seemed to be running his affairs on naval lines. Having flown to Paris on his own, he put me on a standby call with instructions to be packed and ready to join him at a moment's notice. I didn't take him seriously, of course. A man of settled years doesn't wish to be sent rocketing about his business without due warning, so when he phoned from Paris at breakfast time to say that I had to be at Heathrow in half an hour, I wasn't pleased.

I made it, in fact, but when I got to Paris I disobeyed an instruction to wait for him at our hotel, and went instead to a café round the corner. Once he tracked me down, I refused to speak for half an hour, causing him to go to work like Bosun Grieg when I threatened to report him to my mother.

After the shopping spree, however, and a promise that we could eat that night in a sandwich bar instead of a disgusting *haute cuisine* establishment, I thawed out slightly, felt mellow enough indeed to say how jolly it must be for him and Lovering to be abroad with such a nice old party.

'In fact you're impossible,' said Chapman. 'The most difficult man I've ever worked with. If things go wrong . . .'

Mrs Mouse was Out and About

When my vacuum cleaner broke down this week, I asked one of the chaps in the *Root Into Europe* office – Catey Sexton (my favourite), as it happened – if she had any advice on how to mend it. This was clumsy of me, I suppose, since – with smart technology sprouting from every pocket – she was hooked up or patched in, or whatever, with seven different countries at the time, working out a shooting schedule for *Root Into Europe*, compared with which planning Sir Stormin' Norman's recent desert evolutions would have seemed like a day at the beach.

'What's a vacuum cleaner?' she said. 'Excuse me, I must get on.'

I should have asked one of the girls, of course: Lovering or Chapman, or even our producer, Justin Judd. Judd, as you know, recently married Mrs Bear and must, as a consequence, have become practised in domestic science. After a hard day at the office, Mrs Bear wouldn't take kindly, I imagine, to finding her home less than spick and span.

Be that as it may, I wasn't surprised by Catey's inability to help me, though my colleague Jim White might have been, I think. In his column last week, Mr White, you may remember, heartbreakingly compared his carefree bachelor days – when the fridge had cultures growing in it and the bathroom looked as if a horse had been the last to use it – with his present married state which, alarmingly, seems to entail a fridge full of yoghurt made from kiwi fruit and a bath with children in it.

Either Mr White has been most unfortunate, or I've been very clever. Women, in my experience, have no aptitude for housework whatsoever. If you want a housekeeper, hire a man and have the job done properly – and that, from time to time, has been my policy.

When I first lived in London I used to drink gin with Indian poets and, wishing to become a ballet critic, to take tea with Dicky Buckle. I had little time to make the beds and so forth, so I let rooms in my house to Morse and Robertson.

Morse and Robertson were City gents and, after fooling about at the Stock Exchange, had energy enough to put on comic aprons and cook a meal, thereafter wearing rubber gloves to do the washing up. Men can get away with this sort of stuff, but women look ridiculous in rubber gloves and aprons. Women should work, that's what they're good at (building up businesses and so forth) and when they're not working they should rest demandingly in bed ('I'm bored. Could you hop out and get me some magazines?'). After Morse and Robertson I therefore sought out women who were too bushed at the end of the day to cook a meal or Hoover under your feet.

After a couple of air shots I was lucky, or clever enough, to meet Jacqui the Dancer, a soloist with the Royal Ballet. Ballet dancers work like pit ponies and are, therefore, ideal partners. They practise their *pliés* all day in a long mirrored room under the stern gaze of an arthritic Russian lady with a stick and in the evening they perform at Covent Garden. With any luck you won't see them at all and you won't catch them wearing rubber gloves. I suppose I had a meal ready for Jacqui the Dancer when she got home at midnight, but I can't remember what.

After that, I was fortunate enough to live with a hard-working film actress who had a reputation for being difficult. In her early days she had narrowly failed to get the lead in a West End show, whereupon she had eaten her mother's carpet. I liked the sound of that – ambitious and petulant – so I became her butler for a while.

Apart from cooking and cleaning my main task was to edit the morning papers, since any mention in them of Susannah York or Julie Christie – serious rivals at the time – caused her to chew the carpet. I must have been good at the job because a production company was obliged to fly me to Ireland once, following a complaint that the service she was getting in a Dublin five-star hotel wasn't up to scratch.

Then there was Mrs Mouse. Mrs Mouse was fun to be with – not that I often was. Mrs Mouse didn't work, as far as I know, but she had a lot of young friends and was out and about most of the time. Hoping for an opportunity to whack an actor, I used to track her at a surveillance operator's distance and, as a consequence, the housework suffered. I sought out Morse and Robertson – hoping to re-employ them in the kitchen – but when I discovered that they now had domestic obligations of their own I hired a firm of private investigators to track Mrs Mouse on a full-time basis, releasing me to do the housework.

Those were the days, and if I say I wouldn't have had this problem with my vacuum cleaner had my third wife not walked out on me, I mean no disrespect. Apart from an ability to strip down electrical appliances and reassemble them in working order, she was perfect. But she isn't with me any more, so I turned to Catey – with foreseeable consequences. Never mind. Mrs Bear has granted Mr Bear a two-hour break from his other duties, and he'll have my Hoover mended in a jiffy.

Only a Nerd Talks *to Tanit*

I don't know what your method of doing business is, but mine is to appoint an intermediary between me and the person who wishes to engage my services, thereafter instructing the latter to ignore anything the former says – to deal with me, in fact, since the intermediary is clearly mad. Cat Ledger, my temporary literary agent, has, as a consequence, been somewhat at a disadvantage when negotiating with Justin Judd, the producer of *Root Into Europe*, and from time to time Judd, too, has been a little confused, I think.

To Cat Ledger I say: 'Let's shaft these chaps. We've got them over a barrel here.' And then I sidle up to Judd and say: 'A word in your ear, old bean. Between you and me, the woman's off her rocker. We're artists, you and I. I'll sign anything you put in front of me.'

I'm laughing, but Ledger and Judd are scarcely on speaking terms. Mention of Judd's name causes Ledger to take two days off in Wales, and if Ledger's name crops up, Judd turns as white as herring roe and whimpers, was found once in the office pantry with a saucepan on his head, said recently that he'd prefer to remove his own appendix with an oyster fork than deal again with Ledger.

On Monday I swore blind to Ledger that I wouldn't sign my associate producer contract until she'd renegotiated a clause or two, whereupon Judd threatened to take me off a plane to Ibiza – sending Mark Chapman there without me – unless I signed it on the spot.

This was serious. Chapman is a good egg and a brilliant director, but he won't mind my saying that he isn't an Ibiza type. Some are, some aren't. I am. It's to do with the hips and trousers, an ability to move with ease below the waist, to walk around with the heavily medicated aspect of an out-patient on the Minnesota Method.

In the course of our researches, Chapman and I have persuaded many important people – politicians, senior police officers, High Court judges – to appear as themselves in *Root Into Europe*, but none has the stature of Tanit, the Island God of Ibiza, and I could scarcely expect Chapman on his own to secure him for our series. I therefore signed the contract.

Tanit is the heavy centre of Ibiza's in-set, a massively composed almost-naked Negro, who came out of the sea ten years ago proclaiming himself to be a god – more accurately, in fact, pitched up from Germany with his pal, El Pimpo, an enormous Italian with a head no bigger than a lemon, and with six working girls in tow.

Stone nude except for a powder-blue, bejewelled *cache-sexe*, he now pads silently round Ibiza town as if expecting applause, as if there's an audience, which there always is. Flying to Ibiza, I told Chapman how to comport himself if Tanit deigned to speak to us.

'I'm particularly keen,' I said, 'that he doesn't mistake us for two nerds who normally take their holidays in the Dordogne or Tuscany. It would be better, therefore, if you didn't seek his opinion of the latest Alan Ayckbourn play, ask him for the name of an agreeable restaurant, or offer him a glass of bubbly. I'm worried, too, about your trousers. They seem to date from November 1989, if not October.'

'Never mind my trousers,' said Chapman. 'Where will we find him?'

'Tanit,' I said, 'has the divine attribute of being everywhere at once. Whatever time it is – day or night – Tanit is where you are. Asked once by someone when he slept, Tanit replied: "I sleep when you sleep" – a difficult claim to contradict.'

'And then you'll speak to him?'

I was flabbergasted. 'You don't *speak* to Tanit. You don't blunder up to him and say, "Hello, old bean." That would be a *faux pas*, like starting up a conversation with the Queen –

something, I may say, that my friend Craig Brown once did. He buttonholed her at a garden party, told her a joke involving Kafka, showed her a hole in his trousers. He went to Eton, of course.'

'It's a pity,' said Chapman, 'that your friend Mr Brown isn't with us now. What language does Tanit speak?'

'Mine,' I said. 'You may not understand.'

Once in Ibiza, we found Tanit almost at once – as I said we would – dining with his entourage at Pacha where, to my horror, Chapman bounced up to him and introduced himself.

'Jolly good show, old bean,' said Tanit. 'Great admirer of your work, *Wax on Wheels*, was it? *On the Piste*? I barked with laughter. How can I help you?'

'I'd like you to be in my new series, *Root Into Europe*.'

'I'd be delighted,' Tanit said. 'Hope you don't shoot in August, though. In August I like to take a short break in the Dordogne. Catch up on my reading, eat like a pig, what? I like your trousers, by the way. Boss, are they? Damn nice. You'll have to speak to my agent, of course. Cat Ledger. Splendid woman. Care for a glass of bubbly?'

Chapman is still in Ibiza with his new pal, Tanit the Island God, but I returned to London, stopping in duty free to buy a set of oyster forks for Justin Judd.

To Santa Eulalia in Search of Chapman

An unseemly game of musical chairs took place in the *Root Into Europe* office on Monday morning as the beneficiaries of Mark Chapman's disappearance in Ibiza – his failure, at least, to return to London – scrimmaged for preferment round the boardroom table.

Jenny Zamit had, by 9 a.m. already installed herself, with chairman's gavel and *aide-memoire*, in Chapman's seat, only to be removed from it by Justin Judd who, after a short burst on the subject of bad taste and so forth, barged the rest of us out of his path – myself, Rachel Salter, Jeremy Lovering, Luke Schiller, the assistant director, and my new best friend Pablo Behrens, our Uruguayan location manager – and sat in it himself. The only absentee was Catey Sexton who had taken her smart technology to Dover for the day.

'Right,' said Judd. 'A sad occasion and so forth. A fine man, Chapman, and a competent director. Gave us all our first break. No doubt we're grateful to him. That's enough of that. They come and they go. One door closes and another opens. Every cloud, etc.'

'Spilt milk,' said Jenny.

'Water under the bridge,' said Schiller.

'The show must go on,' said Rachel.

'Precisely,' said Judd. 'Albeit a different one. With Chapman gone, we can junk *Root Into Europe*. Never cared for it myself. On to the next. Revolving credit. Back to back. Here's one . . .'

'Just a minute,' said Lovering. 'Aren't we being a little hasty here? A lot of work's gone into this.'

'Good man,' I said. 'It's a relief that someone feels loyalty to the enterprise.'

'Stuff the enterprise,' said Lovering. 'My loyalty is to my European wardrobe. I've acquired a different ensemble for each location.'

'I agree,' said Schiller. 'With a new director, *Root Into Europe* could still survive.'

'Here, here,' said Jenny, slipping into Judd's seat – previously Chapman's – as Judd momentarily left the room. 'In my experience, directors grow on trees.'

'Exactly,' said Schiller. 'I myself . . .'

'*You?*' said Lovering. 'Your taste's deplorable. At last week's press launch you wore a Next tie with a Katharine Hamnett jacket!'

It seemed likely that Schiller and Lovering might come to blows, so it was fortunate that Pablo Behrens, our Uruguayan location manager, intervened.

'*Chapman es un buen loco*,' he said. '*Podriamos localizarlo y mandar un equipo de rescate a la selva.*'

'I wish you'd learn to speak English,' Jenny said. 'Small wonder the French scenes now take place in Germany, and the Italian ones in Turkey.'

Pablo had suggested, I think, that a rescue party be despatched to Ibiza in search of Chapman, and it was decided, after a short discussion, that Pablo and I – since it was we who had last seen Chapman, dancing in Pacha with his new pal, Tanit the Island God – should undertake this mission.

'Have you any idea what might have happened to him?' asked Judd, who had now returned to the boardroom. 'My seat, I think, Miss Zamit.'

'*Podria ser – me perdona – la bebida, lamentablemente*,' said Pablo.

A ripple of shock ran round the table. With the exception of myself, no one here was old enough to have lost a child to the alcohol culture, to have watched helplessly as a son or daughter sweated and told jokes, left comic announcements on their answerphones and drove their sports cars into bollards, but the others might have parents who trembled at six o'clock and poured a gin and tonic, who wore tights in public and took part in amateur dramatics, often *Iolanthe*.

Rachel was the first to find her voice.

'Surely that sort of thing doesn't happen in Ibiza?' she said.

'Not in Ibiza town,' I said. 'But in Santa Eulalia there are hellholes – on a par with the Groucho Club and the Coach and Horses – where watery-eyed English alcoholics stand in groups and boast unhappily to one another, as if auditioning for *Jeffrey Bernard is Unwell*. Outings are laid on from Ibiza town so that well-behaved young people – on nothing more antisocial than crack or Ecstasy – can look at them and learn.'

'You didn't go to one of these bars, I hope,' said Judd.

'I'm afraid we did.'

Pablo and I were sent to Ibiza on the next flight. We went straight to Santa Eulalia, but Chapman was nowhere to be found.

The next day we returned to London where Catey seemed to be in charge.

'You're a couple of puddings,' she said. 'While I was in Dover, Chapman kept in touch with me through my smart technology. He's in Italy at the moment. Where's Pablo, by the way?'

'He's . . . well I never! He was with me a second ago. I must have left him in Santa Eulalia. Never mind. He can't speak English and . . .'

'You've got half an hour to get to the airport,' Catey said.

Kindly Fax the Menu, Pedro

If, instead of my column, the menu at the Café Royale, Santa Eulalia, is published here this week, avoid the *pollo Ibicenco*, that's my advice. I'll explain why later – if I remember, if I'm sober.

Meanwhile, you'll want to know how I and my young friends celebrated Cole Porter's centenary on Saturday – not that it's any of your damn business. I missed my own party in his honour, that's how – the one my literary agent, Alison, and I had been planning for a year.

Big deal. Terence Blacker brought his amplifier and a bulging portfolio of work in progress, and offered the others a choice: either he'd sing 'Don't Fence Me In' to his own accompaniment or he'd read extracts from his latest novel. It was nineteen out of twenty for 'Don't Fence Me In', I'm told, with my best friend Little Jo abstaining. 'I think I'll have an early night,' she said.

You'll excuse the rather ungenerous tone of this, but I tied one on last night, had a skinful, in fact, and now I'm paying the price. It's 9 a.m. and I'm sitting outside the Café Royale, Santa Eulalia, my head's rotting on the inside and I seem to have lost a shoe, but if Pedro there would bring me another double vodka I'd be all right. I'm keen, meanwhile, to fax this to London on the menu – while I'm sober, while I can remember where I am and why. I'm a pro, trained to fax and file from bars at all hours.

What a night though! One minute I was doing a Coral Browne impression in Sandy's Bar ('They opened her up, darling, but all they found was Tallulah Bankhead's gardening glove') and the next a fat actor and I, wearing girls' hats and with our trousers rolled up above the knee (you'd have laughed if you'd been there) were leading a conga down the street, there-after driving, uncertainly, to San Antonio in search of totties, preferably Swedish. We found them too, bore down on them amusingly, but they didn't seem to have a sense of humour, became quite aggressive, in fact, and told us to push off. Lesbians, I suppose – so often the case these days, what with the feminist movement and subsidized art and so forth. Mozart didn't need a grant, nor did Shakespeare – incomparable artists both. Anyway – after that we cried a bit and went to bed.

Where was I? 'Chop chop Pedro!' That's better. I know, I have it now. Last week, Catey Sexton, the brains behind *Root Into Europe*, sent me back to Ibiza to look for Pablo Behrens, our Uruguayan location manager, who had himself become lost in the search for Mark Chapman, our director as was.

I didn't fancy that at all. It would mean going to Santa Eulalia, mixing with English actors and alcoholics in Sandy's Bar which, in thirty years of coming to Ibiza, I'd only entered once. On that occasion – because I didn't drink and had no anecdotes at my disposal – I was dubbed a wind-up merchant (not an expression I'd actually heard used before) and shown the door.

I'm not one to make the same mistake twice, so this time I had with me on the plane *Knock Me Down with a Stage Weight!* by Christopher Biggins and Jack Tinker (Arthur Barker, £9.50) and Dirk Bogarde's *Book of Ripostes* (Chatto and Windus, £15.95). I read these carefully during the flight but couldn't see the point at all, and eventually sought advice from the lady sitting next to me.

'Here's one, madam,' I said. 'Invited by the director to sit on a plinth, Bea or Boo – whoever they might be – said: "Certainly, darling. Plinth Charles or Plinth Philip?" What do you make of that?'

'Your delivery's wrong,' she said. 'If you wish to be a raconteur, you must learn to deploy the fat humorous words appropriate to the genre, the heavy fruity adverbs – avidly balefully, unceremoniously – and the portly nouns – thespian, individual, quip, protagonist. Thus. "You must be out of your tiny Chinese mind", riposted Bea (or Boo) balefully, and the unfortunate individual was unceremoniously ejected! Do you drink?'

'Certainly not,' I said – indeed, I hadn't touched a drop since I discovered, years ago, that alcohol rots the brain cells at the rate of a million a minute, that the brain shrinks to the size of a plum, the skull caves in and eventually you swallow your head. I saw it happen to my father.

'That's your second mistake,' she said.

I had one then – a double vodka – and I won't appear smart or boastful, I hope, or to be encouraging old folk on the downward path, if I say that the effect is instantaneous. The head swims, the legs go and you sit on a chair which isn't there. Then you sweat a bit and start to cry. This doesn't matter, since the remedy's to hand – you immediately have another.

Last night I was most amusing in Sandy's Bar and today some Dereks and I have taken over the bull ring for a comic cricket match. They'll come and get me, I suppose. They'll be out here from the *Root Into Europe* office, judging me irreplaceable. Meanwhile, this is the life, I can handle it, I can . . . excuse me, the *pollo Ibicenco*'s coming back, I think. 'Pedro!'

You Can Reach Me at Sandy's Bar

I'm still in Santa Eulalia and, over breakfast in Sandy's Bar the other day, Denholm Elliot said I was drinking too much.

'You're running away from something,' he said.

'I'm not running away from anything,' I said. 'I'll return to London just as soon as I'm ready. I know what I'm doing. I can handle it.'

Denholm happens to be a great mate and one of my favourite actors – quite unaffected, quite unspoilt – otherwise I'd have told him to mind his own damn business. Why, if I was running away, would I have published my whereabouts in my piece last week, thus allowing every commissioning editor in London to track me down? (Leave a message at Sandy's Bar if you want to join the queue. I come in at 10 a.m. for my breakfast vodka, unless I've been drinking the night before, in which case I come in at 9 a.m for what we call the hair of the dog. I might ring you back, but in all likelihood won't.)

They've all been on: a chap from the *Daily Telegraph* who, according to Sandy, liked my remarks last week on subsidized art and now wants me to do a Thursday think-piece for his paper; two publishers – one called Sidey, the other Percy Bantam-Smith, or something of the sort; and a couple of characters from the BBC – a woman from Sue Lawley's office inviting me to appear on *Desert Island Discs* and a television producer who wants me to do an episode in the *Byline* series. It seems that, in last week's programme, Judge Pickles argued for the legalization of hard drugs and now they would like me to present the opposing view.

I didn't speak to any of them. Heaven knows who Bantam-Smith and Sidey are, but I'm tempted by *Desert Island Discs* by the chance to take on Pickles and by the *Telegraph* offer. The latter would give me an opportunity to assert the divine pre-eminence of old Bill Shakespeare (a conduit, surely, through whom God spoke to the world) and, more importantly, to line up behind Mary Kenny against theory-ridden academics such as Roland Barthes ('the bloke can't write,' said Miss Kenny incomparably – and devastatingly – in last week's *Sunday Telegraph*) and Professor Terry Eagleton ('and nor can he!'). As for Pickles, he should know that cannabis leads inevitably to cocaine and heroin – which kill you instantly – further, that even though it doesn't, and even though they don't, so what?

Meanwhile, I had another double vodka and started to draw up a list of the records I'd ask for on *Desert Island Discs*, shortly seeking Denholm Elliot's assistance in compiling this.

'I'm soon to appear on *Desert Island Discs*,' I said, 'and am keen to refute the theory that because a fellow drinks too much and is practically a half-wit his taste in music is likely to begin and end with Herman and the Hermits. I'd be grateful, therefore, if you'd jot down some stuff by Mozart, Vivaldi and so forth.'

While Denholm was doing this, Sandy said that Percy Bantam-Smith was on the phone again. I was in a pretty good mood by now, so I thought I'd see what he wanted.

'Yes?' I said. 'Who the hell are you?'

'Patrick Jansen-Smith,' he said. 'Corgi Books. I publish your friend Terence Blacker.'

'That's nothing to boast about,' I said. 'I don't like Blacker, never have, so I probably wouldn't like you.'

'I thought your piece last week was much better than usual,' he said. 'Is it the drink, do you think?'

'Probably,' I said. 'Read it again when you're sober.'

'I particularly enjoyed the quips from Dirk Bogarde's *Book of Ripostes*. Plinth Charles or Plinth Philip! I'm keen to commission *Great Theatrical Anecdotes* for my Christmas humour list. What do you say?'

I said I'd think about it and later asked Denholm Elliot to stop drawing up a list of composers for *Desert Island Discs* and instead to trawl his brain for comic ripostes.

This was good, I'd never been in such demand. But a small, as yet unidentified, anxiety began to tug uncomfortably at the edges of my fuddled mind. Something was missing, someone hadn't rung who should've done. Then it struck me that no one from the *Root Into Europe* office had tried to get in touch with me. That was odd. We shoot in two weeks' time and if they think they can manage without me they're making a big mistake. I'll not ring them, however. If they want me they can come and get me.

I had another vodka but it didn't work. I hit rock bottom, began, in my self-pity, to think about my literary agent, Alison, of her youthful indifference, her thrilling unconcern. I took out some copies of her school reports, which I always carry in my wallet, and tapped Denholm on the shoulder.

'Would you like to see my beloved's school reports?' I said. 'Look – she came top in art and showed promise in . . . Oh God, I miss her,' and I started to cry.

'You're drinking too much' Denholm said. 'You're running away from something.'

'Mind your own damn business,' I said.

Blanked by Jenny, Whom I've Never Liked

I'm still in Santa Eulalia, but I'll be returning to London soon, I think. The tourists are beginning to find their way to Sandy's Bar – taxi drivers from Chelmsford, gross women clutching tasteless souvenirs, louts in ghastly Gazza haircuts who wouldn't know Mozart from Maradona. Surely it was Amis *père* who hymned of 'Memento-bibbers, randy on Mustique?' He should have said Ibiza.

They even bring their kids in. Don't get me wrong, I like kids, but I don't want them in my local. You can't take it away from Mrs Thatcher (she broke the mould), but you have to admit that she made it viable for these disagreeable people to spoil Europe for the rest of us. They've even reached Tuscany, I'm told. At least the Americans haven't got here yet.

Which reminds me. The worst thing about being a bit well known is that every crashing bore from Essex thinks he's got the bloody right to start a conversation. I was in Sandy's Bar the other night having just the one with my friend the Bishop of Santa Eulalia (he's quite a character – a disqualified solicitor from Fetter Lane who was informed by the Law Society, when they struck him off, that it was customary for officers of the court to advise their clients after they'd committed an offence rather than before – but that's another story and one, incidentally, to which only the creator of the immortal *Rumpole of the Bailey* could do full justice) when this taxi driver with a kid in tow prodded me in the chest and said he'd heard me on *Desert Island Discs* last week and then called me a pseud for choosing as my castaway's reading Dryden's *Dunciad*.

A pseud is one thing I'm not, thank God – I've got a saving sense of humour and am far too ready to laugh at myself to be a pseud – so I didn't give a stuff for his opinion. On top of which, I can't have been too bad because your letters have been very kind, thanks, and it was nice of the BBC to let me do it down the line from Santa Eulalia. Nice, too, of Sandy to keep me well supplied with vodka during the recording.

Which reminds me. Godfrey Smith, who must have read here that I'm working on *Great Theatrical Anecdotes* for Percy Bantam-Smith of Corgi Books, has just sent me a delicious putdown by the Master. Noel was walking along Piccadilly when he was wolf-whistled by a cab rank. Noel tapped one of the cheery cabbies on the shoulder with his rolled umbrella and cracked inimitably: 'Disappear, naughty taxi driver!' (Thank you, Godders, there's a bottle of bubbly on its way.)

Which brings me back to the taxi driver who called me a pseud in Sandy's Bar. Not having the Master's inimitable riposte at my fingertips, I told him to mind his business and, with my evening thoroughly spoilt, I wandered off for something to eat. I must have been a bit depressed, had momentarily lost my saving sense of humour, I suppose, because I passed out in the restaurant, fell face down in a bowl of gazpacho, later woke up in the street with blood on my shirt and short-term memory loss.

I had a long hard look at myself, at what had happened to me in the last few weeks. Perhaps I *was* drinking too much, perhaps it was only misplaced pride which had prevented me from getting in touch with the *Root Into Europe* office. They were probably out of their minds with worry, in all likelihood didn't read the *Independent* so would have no idea what had become of me, might, more seriously, have cancelled the series, realizing that without my mature, controlling artistic presence it would swiftly descend into facetiousness and bathos. I have enough feathers in my hat, but the others depended on me. I returned to my room and had a shower, and later – having refused just the one in Sandy's Bar – rang the office collect. Unfortunately, I got Jenny Zamit, whom I've never liked.

'It's William,' I said.

'William who?' she said.

'Donaldson,' I said. 'I'd like to speak to Mark Chapman.'

'Can you tell me what it's in connection with?' she said.

'*Root Into Europe*,' I said.

'Just a moment,' she said. There was a bit of faffing around in the background – audible whispers and so forth – and then she was on the line again.

'He's a bit tied up at the moment,' she said. 'Could you ring back later?'

I didn't bother. Sod the lot of them. I've heard how writers are treated by film folk but I don't propose to follow the example of Ernest Hemingway (Ernest was my sort of man and a great writer, incidentally) who, to quote the bard, challenged God's fiat 'gainst self slaughter', and blew his and Zelma's brains out.

Anyway, I should worry. Next week a researcher from the BBC is coming out to Santa Eulalia to discuss my contribution to the *Byline* series; I've been asked to do four *Spectator* 'diaries' and with your help (a bottle of bubbly for any which are used) I'll have *Great Theatrical Anecdotes* to Percy Bantam-Smith within the month.

'I'll have that double vodka now,' I said to Sandy.

I can handle it.

Monkeys, Crack and Georgie Cookson

I will be coming back to London next week, thanks, ironically, to Sidey – one of the many publishers, you may remember, who have been hounding me in Ibiza. Remind me to tell you how this happened. Meanwhile, the BBC has cancelled my contribution to its *Byline* series, the one in which I was to counter Judge Pickles's arguments in favour of legalizing hard drugs.

I should worry. It's a nice question, in my opinion, as to who are the greater idiots: those who appear on the goggle box or those who watch it. In Sandy's Bar we make our own entertainment. Last night the Bishop of Santa Eulalia broke the record for eating hard-boiled eggs and then Georgie Cookson (one of my favourite actresses and a woman, incidentally – and most unusually – who is prepared to stand her round) showed us how to remove a fellow's underwear without disturbing his trousers.

Anyway, they sent a researcher out to Ibiza, an Indian bloke called Anwar something, who turned out to be a bit of a prig, one of those *Guardian*-reading do-gooders who infest every department of the Beeb these days. I think he must have been a member of that ghastly organization called Drinkwatch, a collection of humourless busybodies who think they know what's good for us better than we know it ourselves.

Anyway, we'd arranged to meet in Sandy's Bar, so I'd had just the one, and then another one, and then I fell into one of those black depressions – which is happening more and more often, I don't know why – and then I took out my literary agent Alison's school reports, which I always carry in my wallet, and passed them around the bar.

'You'll want to read my baby's school reports,' I said. 'Her final one is particularly ironic. "I fear for Alison's future," the Mother Superior wrote. Ha! My baby's doing brilliantly, has already built up one of the most successful garden-design businesses in London, so nuns know zip, right?'

Don't get me wrong. I count myself a Christian, possess, like my friend Andrew Wilson, a keen sense of the mystery of things (are we to believe that Shakespeare's *Hamlet, The Marriage of*

Figaro and Chartres Cathedral are the result of random movements of atoms?), but I draw the line at organized religion. Anyway, the thought of my beloved, of her youthful, bruising candour, her feline unconcern, made me cry (as always) and, at that moment, Anwar something walked into Sandy's Bar.

Well, he did most of the talking, outlined Pickles's case (which I hadn't heard, thank God) – the so-called beneficial consequences of the Dutch model and of Dr John Marks's liberal policies in Liverpool (the improvement in addicts' health, the decline in drug-related crime and so forth) – and suggested how I might answer it.

I was as unimpressed as you'd have been. 'You can prove anything with statistics,' I said. 'We all know what heroin and cocaine can do.'

'And with great respect,' Anwar something said, with that immeasurably irritating BBC smart-alec sneer to which, during the Gulf crisis, we grew all too accustomed, alas, on the faces of the Dimblebys and Paxman, 'we can see in your case the effect of alcohol on an empty head.'

'That's as may be,' I riposted, 'but it's nothing compared with the effect of crack on monkeys. Scientists in America (where else!) have recently discovered that, whereas monkeys won't voluntarily smoke nicotine, pot or heroin, once they freebase they won't stop.

'One monkey, in a controlled experiment in California, having freebased for the first time, went up a tree with his equipment – money belt, pipe, bunsen burner, little box of matches – and wouldn't come down. He would not eat, he neglected his appearance, abandoned his family responsibilities and supported his habit with criminal behaviour – theft, extortion and so forth. Quite desocialized, do you see?'

'All your example proves,' said Anwar something, 'is that monkeys shouldn't freebase. Rats, equally, are seldom at their best on vodka.' And then he left.

How absurd. It must be obvious to the meanest intelligence that there is no correlation between the effects of alcohol and those of hard drugs; society accepts one but not the other and we all know what happened when the US experimented with prohibition in the twenties.

Anyway, I should worry. Since I started drinking, your flatter-

113

ing letters have been pouring in, the *Mail on Sunday* wants me to do a weekly think-piece and Percy Bantam-Smith of Corgi Books will be pleased to know that *Great Theatrical Anecdotes* is almost ready for the printers.

Which reminds me. A bottle of bubbly is on its way to that splendid actor John Neville – remember him? – who has sent me this from darkest Canada.

'In 1954,' writes John, 'Dickie Burton and I were alternating the parts of Othello and Iago at the Old Vic. At one performance Dickie would play the boastful Moor and I the diabolically clever NCO, and at the next we'd switch. All went according to plan until we lunched rather too well at the Ivy one day.

'Staggering out of the restaurant a little the worse for wear, we returned to the theatre for a matinée and both played Iago! The audience noticed nothing unusual and nor (in the state we were in) did we.'

Delicious, John! Anyway, soon after Anwar something had walked out, Sandy said my publisher was on the line. Thinking he meant Percy Bantam-Smith, I walked right into it. It wasn't Bantam-Smith, but this bloke Sidey. Next week I'll tell you who he is, and why he is bringing me back to London – if I remember, if I'm sober. Meanwhile, I've got to do my think-piece for the *Mail on Sunday*. Cheers!

Great Theatrical Anecdotes *for Percy Bantam-Smith*

Paul Sidey of Random Century – one of the many publishers who have been hounding me in Ibiza – isn't as silly as he looks. Not that he looks particularly silly; indeed he doesn't look silly at all. A little too well preserved, perhaps, for a literary man of a certain age, a little too crisp in the step and upper head; more like an old-time actor – even, in a certain light, like a retired soloist with the Ballet Rambert – but he'll know his business best.

A week ago, in order to get my memoirs out of me (already a year late in the delivery), he booked me into a rehabilitation clinic by the sea, one of those in which, if it practises the dreaded Minnesota Method, the first thing they do (after they've confiscated your cash and credit cards, your shoe laces and portfolio of funding stock) is to sit you down at a school desk in the company of others and – with the threat that if your efforts are less than candid you'll be on all fours swabbing the latrines – make you write out your life story in a large red exercise book. You then stand on a podium and read it out, your construction and syntax and, indeed, your life thereafter being ridiculed by the assembled derelicts, also by your counsellor, a merciless Christian with demented eyes.

Sidey, having come to some arrangement with the clinic, hoped, I imagine, to publish my exercise book on which he would be spared the usual editorial exertions, since it had already been closely worked on by my fellow patients.

Like Boy George, Betty Ford and that silly old tart from Hollywood who, in her memoirs, recently and quite unnecessarily criticized Goldie Hawn on the score of her unwashed hair, I have, in a nutshell, been to hell and back, am now merely at the crossroads.

I could go up or down – the choice is mine. Obviously, as a recovering alcoholic, I can't continue to fax think-pieces from a bar to the *Daily Telegraph* and the *Mail on Sunday*, eat prawn avocado in a large hotel, thereafter discussing publicly with John Mortimer and Taki the question of 'Censorship and the Craft of Letters' or complete *Great Theatrical Anecdotes* for Percy Bantam-Smith, but, more importantly, I can face myself in the mirror and say: 'I like me.'

Last week, you may remember, I was having just the one in Sandy's Bar, when Sandy said my publisher was on the telephone. Thinking he meant Percy Bantam-Smith I took the call and was a little thrown to discover it was Sidey on the line.

'Why are you hounding me?' I said. 'I'm aware that your fine old imprint has recently been gobbled up by men in suits and barmy jumped-up women with names like Ros, but I had assumed that an old-time type like you would give an artist creative elbow-room. I'll deliver my memoirs when I'm ready.'

Sidey said he couldn't care less about my memoirs, he was ringing in fact on behalf of Simon Carr. Carr is an old friend whom I put up with for the sake of Susan, his wife, of whom I'm very fond. He possesses a quick, if superficial wit, which – in order to add pepper and salt to my own weightier reflections – I've never been too proud to plagiarize.

'As you know,' said Sidey, 'we recently – and to great acclaim – published Carr's first novel *The Hop Quad Dolly*. You're on record as saying it's the funniest book you've ever read.'

'Can't remember that,' I said. 'Short-term memory loss. It's the drink, you see.'

Sidey then outlined his plan which was that he would fly me back to London if I agreed to undertake a publicity tour as Carr who, inconveniently, had chosen this moment to move his business to New Zealand. Carr, it seemed, had already been booked to appear on various radio shows in which he would discuss humour and so forth with a cross-section of provincial disc jockeys and other guests – mad women on a diet, chaps about to ride a wheelbarrow across the Kalahari desert. I would appear, more or less, as Carr, advertising the title of his novel rather as a tennis pro hops on to court with brand names pinned about his person.

I agreed and, two days later, Sidey flew me back to London, thereafter sending me to Weston-super-Mare where, prior to appearing the next day on Radio Avon, he booked me into an hotel called Broadway Lodge.

Hotel my foot. Sidey had tricked me in order to get my memoirs. The place was a rehabilitation clinic for alcoholics, as I realized instantly when a mad-eyed Christian at the entrance took away my cash and luggage and told me to doss down in a dormitory. I spent one night in the company of the most boring men I've ever met: three airline pilots, an actor, a brain surgeon and a disinherited aristocrat or two; and in the morning I did a runner.

I rang Sidey when I got back to London. 'If you think I can't tell the difference between a provincial hotel and a rehabilitation clinic,' I said, 'you're sillier than you look.'

'Who's silly?' Sidey said. 'For the price of an airline ticket you've devoted your whole column to *The Hop Quad Dolly*, £11.99 and a steal at the price.'

Cold-eyed Christians at Broadway Lodge

Wasn't it Anna Raeburn who said 'there's no such thing as a personality transplant'? She meant, I think, that addiction's a disease for which there isn't a cure (the proof consists of some experiments involving rats and vodka) and only a shallow mind, itself incurably addicted to Rylean logic chopping, would find the concept of a personality with a lesion problematic (the ghost in the machine, surely, can also catch a cold) or ask why, if only a set minority of people is vulnerable to this disease, some drugs – Valium and nicotine, for instance – are so much more addictive than others, such as heroin and alcohol.

These arguments, certainly, would cut as much ice as a feather at Broadway Lodge, the rehabilitation clinic from which I was discharged on Monday. They taught me there that I am merely a recovering alcoholic, that I can't take normal life for granted and, most importantly, that my new dependency – on them and on 'Him up there' (an agreeably matey reference, I think, to a divine being) – must be for life.

There are days – dangerous days – when I think I've won, that I've learnt to control my craving. Perhaps I could have just the one with chums in the Coach and Horses, swop anecdotes with pub playwrights and middle-aged men in gym shoes, knuckle a drinking acquaintance in the ribs and cry 'What brings you here, you old reprobate?', fall unconscious into a bowl of gazpacho at the Groucho Club, thereafter filing a think-piece for the *Daily Telegraph*.

I remember how good it was at the beginning, the exhilaration I experienced the first time I set a saloon bar on a roar by saying, in a Humphrey Bogart voice, 'Of all the gin palaces in all the world . . .', later rolling my trousers above the knee and doing a Coral Browne impression. And then, with my new, honest memory, I remember how bad it had been at the end – face down in a ditch in Santa Eulalia, with blood on my shirt and one shoe missing. Addicts are always addicts. One day at a time. It's up to me.

For this lesson I'm indebted, of course, to my counsellors at

117

Broadway Lodge, to Liz and Jeff and Sue and Bill, who taught me that I must take responsibility for my own life, that the drunk me wasn't really me (though who it was wasn't discussed, which is as well, perhaps, since it would have raised difficult questions of transpersonal identity); nor must I forget true friends – Tel and Little Jo, Tony the Drug Fiend, Jillypoo and Black Simone – who were always there, if at a distance, or those who were not so fortunate – Craig, Françoise, Jamie and Ben – and those whose destinies I do not know, but for whom I pray – Jake, Ian, Henrietta and Timothy. I was lucky; I'm in recovery, but thousands aren't. Out there, airline pilots and High Court judges are going about their business with enough alcohol in their systems to pickle a school of whales.

Meanwhile, should I go back to work? On my last day at Broadway Lodge, Jeff or Bill – I can't remember which – warned me not to.

'Remember,' said Jeff or Bill, 'that you're on the programme for life – and I don't mean *Root Into Europe*. The people producing this are precisely the types you should avoid.'

I wasn't so sure. I'm familiar with the shenanigans showbiz folk get up to after work – unwinding in a pub, having a skinful in the company of sparks, props and the wardrobe lady who often lives in Ealing – but my colleagues in the *Root Into Europe* office (the girls, at least – Chapman, Lovering and Judd) are dull sticks who, after toiling at their desks all day, jog and eat bananas.

The chaps, on the other hand – Rachel Salter, Jenny Zamit and my favourite, Catey Sexton – could be a problem. After work, the chaps like to tie one on, arranged to meet me once, you may remember, in a Soho pub, wore bow-ties which lit up and revolved, arrived with whoopee cushions and displayed a taste for anecdotes. Rachel, however, isn't coming on the shoot, which starts next week, and Jenny hasn't spoken to me since I wrote here that I'd never liked her.

This leaves Catey who could be a disastrous influence. Catey, being four times cleverer than the others in the office (with the possible exception of Rachel and Jenny), becomes bored easily, has in my presence twice suffered a slight lesion of the personality. Having decided to avoid her as much as possible, I went to the office and met her in reception.

'I don't know who I really am,' she said. 'Let's go to the pub.'

I had a Perrier water and then Catey asked me to tell her an anecdote. I said I couldn't, that next it would be impressions.

'You've got a mind like a hundredweight of concrete,' she said. 'I start a conversation and you come in at an angle like a truck. You're the most boring man I've ever met.'

I had a double vodka, began to think she's not a bad old tart, even though she has a piranha fish's teeth which she brushes in the morning after she's sharpened her tongue.

'Here's one,' I said. 'Coral Browne and Dicky Burton . . .'

An Attendant Staff of Crisp Young Women

Since I had planned to pull a fast one by selling the publishing rights in *Root Into Europe* behind the back of its producer, Justin Judd, I was disappointed to discover, on my return to the office after my stay in the rehabilitation clinic, that he had taken advantage of my illness to sell them behind mine. And, if you please, to Geoffrey Strachan of Methuen.

'When I arrived on the literary scene in 1960,' wrote Auberon Waugh in a recent edition of the increasingly scintillating *Literary Review*, 'publishers were amiable people who always got drunk at luncheon, never answered letters and preferred talk of other things than books. In the publishing revolution of the seventies and eighties nearly all these pleasant, idle incompetents were pushed out and their places were taken by unpleasant incompetents who managed to hide their idleness in occasional bouts of officious activity.'

My own experience of the last twenty years – in the course of which I've bucketed backwards and forwards between publishers, some of whom have been commoner and more illiterate than others – leads me to suppose that Mr Waugh hardly overstates the case, though I have discovered two or three with whom you might, without loss of self-esteem, take luncheon (if

119

that's your game) or to whom you could happily entrust a manuscript.

Michael O'Mara, the brilliant young American, cares about books and would talk about them if I gave him half a chance (I prefer to educate him – though it's an uphill task – in the exquisite mysteries of gridiron football). Paul Sidey makes me bark with laughter and I am keeping an eye on Rob Shreeve, who is as bright as a button, supports Derby County and is invariably courteous.

The outstanding exception to the general rule, however, is Geoffrey Strachan who, as much to his embarrassment, I imagine, as to theirs, is much cleverer than his cleverest authors and noticeably a better writer.

I've known Strachan since I published his satirical verses and thoughtful book reviews at Cambridge, a compliment that he returned some years later by publishing my second book, a humorous slim volume called *Letters to Emma Jane*, after which he tossed me overboard.

Since then I have – insensitively, perhaps – been attempting to scramble back on board, determinedly parcelling up a manuscript even as I finish it and sending it to Strachan, who, more often than not, returns it instantly with a letter which, though courteously worded, causes me to yelp and tremble like a whippet in a thunderstorm.

I say more often than not because Strachan, when he's not too busy, I imagine, or because it amuses him to discover how I'm still afloat, sometimes invites me to tea instead of writing.

On these occasions he never once refers to the sad submitted manuscript but instead first tells me what a funny writer he thinks my friend Terence Blacker is and then recounts the same anecdote that, since I've written twenty books, I've now heard twenty times.

'This will amuse you,' he says. 'When invited to speak at seminars on humour, I always read out extracts from *Letters to Emma Jane*, as an example of what not to publish.'

I didn't laugh too heartily the first time he told me this, and now I hardly laugh at all. It hasn't been all one way, however. After the success of *The Henry Root Letters* which, of course Strachan had contemptuously rejected, I said that he must be kicking himself for letting this one go.

'How so?' he said.

'Well,' I said – running out of steam halfway through the sentence, like a man launched in mixed company on a joke which he suddenly realizes has a startingly vulgar punchline, 'it was obviously going to make a lot of – er, excuse me – money.'

'I never doubted that,' said Strachan. 'I simply didn't like it. Blacker was on particularly good form this week, I thought.'

When I discovered that he'd acquired the book rights in *Root Into Europe,* I rang him and said how surprised I was – since Blacker had scarcely had a hand in it – that he found it funny.

'Who says I find it funny?' he said. 'I'm expecting George Cole – a comic actor of genius, and Pat Heywood – one of our finest actresses, to save the day. Meanwhile, I'm doing some rewrites myself which Mark Chapman will have on Friday.'

That's all right, then. Since I am no longer needed as a writer, I can sit back and enjoy my duties as associate producer. While others toil, I will lounge importantly in a canvas chair with my name painted on its back or be transported, I imagine, from agreeable location to agreeable location in a caravan or Winnebago, my occasional notes being taken down in triplicate by an attendant staff of crisp young women.

'Fax this column, if you'd be so good, Ms Casparry. Have you ever thought of becoming an actress, by the way?'

It's good to be back in show business.

With Young Woolford in the Baggage Van

It's not true that my boy Charlie is the stupidest person I ever met. Rather, he doesn't know what day of the week it is, never mind what time; he has no sense of small, unimportant obligations in the offing – like finding somewhere to live – but exists unhurriedly in the present like a cat. That said, if you asked him to pitch up on Tuesday in Dover, say, in time to catch a ferry to France, it's 60–40 he'd be there.

The producers of *Root Into Europe* are unwilling, clearly, to take the same odds on their crew, many of whom are quite long in the tooth and haven't become millionaires (owning yachts and private aeroplanes) without knowing whether it's Friday or Christmas Eve. I had imagined, I suppose, that a few days before the shoot someone from the office would have rung me up and said: 'We kick off on Monday, do you see? I'd be obliged if you could be in Dover at 11 in the morning, more or less. Break a leg, darling.'

All last week, in fact, a blizzard of junk mail – maps, movement orders, timetables, schedules – came through my letterbox, instructing me to be at the office at 5.30 on Monday morning for a pep talk and final kit inspection.

The last time someone told me what to do was in 1958 and I didn't like it then, so after the pep talk (and a sharp reminder that our contracts included a morals clause) I asserted my individuality by telling the producer, Justin Judd, that – since the sounds would not be to my taste – I had decided not to ride with him and the other grown-ups in the company Daimler, but in the VW transporter with my new favourite, Luke Schiller, the assistant director, and the chaps – my ex-favourite, Catey Sexton, and Jenny Zamit.

'If you'd read the latest vehicle allocation order,' Justin said, 'you'd know that your place in the Daimler has been taken by Geoffrey Strachan who wishes to discuss his rewrites with the director. You'll be travelling with young Woolford in the baggage van.'

Woolford, the company runner, is an intimidating young man with whom, until then, I'd had only one conversation and, on that occasion, I'd offended him, I think, by pointing out that in spite of his claim that he'd been to Downside he had working-class legs that would have looked better disputing a 50–50 ball with 'Psycho' Pierce at Upton Park.

Never mind. Since he was only twenty-two his sounds would be acceptable – an assumption shortly blown to the winds by the discovery that they consisted of nothing but Nat King Cole and Doris Day selections – and, with a couple of well-chosen anecdotes, I'd be able to bring it sharply to his attention on the journey that I'd not always been an ex-writer on a thin per diem, but a bit of an executive myself.

'This is a load of bollocks,' I said, as we drove through Blackheath.

Young Woolford's mouth tightened like a cheese-cutter. 'I hope you're not going to be negative,' he said.

'Certainly not,' I said. 'I was merely going to point out that we're being treated like schoolchildren. In all the years I produced West End entertainments – first sending them round the provinces on logistically complicated tours – I never mislaid an *artiste* of note. Disgusted by the final run-through of a musical revue, I did return to London once, however, leaving Leslie Crowther and Dame Moira Lister in Liverpool where, I think, they still may be.'

'That's not funny,' Woolford said. 'Moira Lister and Leslie Crowther are two of my favourite *artistes*. I should say, too, that if you continue to make negative comments about the shoot I shall have to report you to Justin Judd.' Then he put on a Doris Day tape.

Once we were safely on the ferry, I ran all over the place trying to shake the others off, but found myself shepherded back into the fold by my ex-favourite, Catey Sexton, who, clearly, had been given the job of keeping me in line.

Whether I was in line or not seemed to me of no account, since my duties had been taken over by Geoffrey Strachan who stood importantly at Mark Chapman's shoulder while the latter shot an excellently funny scene (since Strachan had rewritten it) involving the ferry's captain and George Cole. Chapman is a perfectionist and we might still be there had not Strachan at last stepped forward with a cry of 'It's a wrap, kids!'; thereafter instructing us to proceed in line astern to Paris where lights out would be at 9.30, after biscuits and hot chocolate served by matron.

On the way in the baggage van young Woolford surprised me by saying how glad he was that I was still his travelling companion.

'You like my anecdotes?' I said.

'Yes,' he said. 'I can learn from them how not to end up like you. Not that there's any chance of that. I have recently, and without the knowledge of Chapman and Judd – so I'd be obliged if you didn't mention this in the *Independent* – set up an international facilities company with your boy Charlie. The first year's results were most encouraging.'

Then he put on a Nat King Cole tape.

Cole Will be on a Banana Boat and I'll be Playing Root

I've always greatly admired Derek Jarman, but he blew it for me by telling Lynn Barber in last week's *Independent on Sunday* that making a film is like giving a party. 'If you want everyone to enjoy themselves,' Mr Jarman said, 'you really have to slave at it.' Later, he told Ms Barber that he never hired anyone, still less fired them.

What do you make of that? Fortunately, the producers of *Root Into Europe* have never subscribed to any such nonsense. Indeed, they customarily fire one person a week to keep the others on their toes. Pondering this on Monday in my suite at the Paris Hilton, I easily calculated that, by the time we'd finished in France, three of our number would have gone for an early bath.

The question was, who? The obvious candidates, it seemed to me, were the director, Mark Chapman, the producer, Justin Judd, and myself. It's always a good thing to fire the director since the cast, particularly, is invariably greatly cheered to see the back of him; and for the producer to sack himself would, obviously, strike a spectacular blow for discipline. Judd, who is looking a little crazy at the moment, might, like a chained rottweiler, suddenly bite his own balls off, I thought, but equally he might, if I stood too close, bite mine off first – a move for which, in my associate producer's hat, I could only applaud him heartily – less heartily, however, as writer of the show.

In the event, I decided that Geoffrey Strachan and Tankybums should be the French leg of the shoot's sacrificial goats.

Strachan's offence, as you know, was to have usurped my writer's place at Chapman's side, but I've not mentioned Tankybums recently, I think. Tankybums is my oldest friend, on top of which the idea for *Root Into Europe* was his – a fact which, irritatingly, he points out to anyone who'll listen. Further, he looks like a film star – specifically Stewart Granger – which is what he was, and while in the normal run of things it's no disadvantage to have someone on board who looks like Stewart Granger, Tankybums – currently employed as the shoot's excellent stills photographer – had already used his old-time charm to make himself the most popular boy in the Lower Remove.

Tankybums had to go, but he's been out of the traps a couple of times, so I decided first to unseat Strachan which would be a piece of cake, I thought. And, indeed, it was. That night, as we lined up for cocoa and biscuits in matron's room, Strachan let slip the news that he was to be joined at the weekend by Mrs Strachan. If that wasn't in breach of the morals clause in our agreement, I'd eat my hat, and a plan – which had the great merit, as far as I could see, of cooking Tankybums's goose as well as Strachan's – fell instantly and fully formed into my mind. I immediately took Tankybums to one side.

'A word in your ear, Tankybums,' I said. 'I gather Geoffrey Strachan plans to have his wife out here. It would be better, I think, if Justin Judd heard this from us – who could argue Strachan's case – than from a troublemaker in the company. You do the talking.'

'I certainly will,' Tankybums said – and he did. Once he'd worked up steam, he gave Judd a frightful burst: 'What's the rule regarding women?'

'We're against them,' said Judd.

'Why, exactly?'

'They're a distraction,' said Judd.

'Really?' said Tankybums. 'So you'll tell Geoffrey Strachan – one of London's most distinguished publishers and a man of a certain age – that he can't have his wife out here?'

'Of course,' said Judd. 'Clause 23b of our contracts specifically states that all or any relations with women – wives, common-law or otherwise, fiancées, beloveds, literary agents, concubines, whether local or flown in – are absolutely banned. Two days may be set aside in Rome, however, when women will be airlifted in under plain cover.'

'I see,' said Tankybums. 'As in a prison drama – *The Dirty Dozen*, say – in which a lorryload of women is brought in once a month to relieve the inmates. Has it occurred to you that *Root Into Europe* is precisely about just such repressed English attitudes?'

125

'Is there anything else?' asked Judd.

'There certainly is,' said Tankybums, '!@£$%¢&*!'

Judd blinked, but he didn't go down, and the upshot was that Strachan got the red card and Tankybums the yellow for impertinence.

I should say, perhaps, that the shoot's going brilliantly, thanks mainly to George Cole who, day and night, is performing miracles. Not for much longer, however. I've just learnt that he's to be joined in the Dordogne next week by Mrs Cole, after which, I imagine, he'll be on a banana boat and I'll be playing Root.

Unless, or until, that is, the authorities discover – by reading about it here – that my literary agent, Alison, is to be with me for the entire Spanish leg of the shoot. After which, I suppose, it will be an early tubbing for me, too.

I bet Derek Jarman never had as much fun as this.

Tankybums is on a Yellow Card

My pal Sparks has asked me to a rave-up. You'll be wondering what a rave-up is – further, what's a Sparks? A week ago I, like you, wouldn't have known one from the other or either from a hole in the road.

Now I can tell you what they are.

Sparks is the one on a shoot who knows his rights, tells jokes which are so startlingly filthy that only a woman would understand them and makes several K (whatever that might be) a week. The Sparks on *Root Into Europe* is a splendid chap, but I'm a little surprised that he's become my special pal. It takes one to know one, I suppose.

In any closed society – a shoot, a school, a frigate or a prison – you need a pal otherwise you'll be walking in a crocodile alone, be taking a half-holiday or run-ashore in the company only of yourself. The important thing, however, is not to choose your pal too soon, else you'll be serving your sentence glued to the wrong chap entirely.

This happened to me at Winchester, I must admit. Alarmed on my first night there by the spectacle of small boys being thrown by grown men out of windows, I made friends instantly with Pode instead of Popper. It then took me two years to find the words with which to end my affair with Pode.

Not that I ever had to use them. One morning Pode approached me after breakfast and said that he'd be walking up to books with Popper. My instinct had been correct, however.

Pode later became headmaster of Shrewsbury and Popper went to prison. Keen, on the shoot, not to make the same mistake, I held myself apart at first while I decided who my special pal would be.

Tankybums, my oldest friend, seemed to be the natural choice, but, as I explained last week, I had plans for him – specifically, to get him fired. Lovering, Luke Schiller (my favourite), Catey Sexton and Jenny Zamit, all of whom are excellent company in the normal run of things, have become prim little podges since we came to France – wearing tight, conscientious faces, oiling up to Judd and Chapman and jogging on the spot while taking orders, their little arms and legs pumping keenly at the double – so I ruled them out.

It was between Young Woolford and Props, I thought, but then I was approached by Sparks, who told me a joke I didn't understand and then asked me to a rave-up in his van.

That got me thinking. I was unclear what a rave-up was, but it sounded as if it would be contrary to standing orders. I'd check this out with Judd, I thought, and – on receiving confirmation that attendance at one would be a serious offence – I'd tell Tankybums (already on a yellow card) that my pal Sparks had asked him to a rave-up in his van, after which I'd arrange to have it busted. I found Judd in conference with Jenny Zamit.

'Excuse me,' I said. 'What's the ruling on rave-ups?'

'Rave-ups are all right,' said Judd. 'In fact we encourage them.'

I was disappointed but I thought I'd find out what they were. 'What are they exactly?'

'A group of men, after hours, often in pantyhose,' said Judd.

'Nothing wrong with that. Ian Botham on tour Down Under comes to mind, also the Duke of York. You're required to have a sense of humour. Drinks are taken, jokes told, intestinal gases lit.

'Boot polish has its uses. I'll not go further. Harmless fun. A chance to let off steam.' 'What about women?' Judd's face clouded over. 'Women?' he said. '*Women*? I'll not have women at a rave-up. A time and a place and so forth. I'll not have women after hours.'

'Jenny's a woman,' I said.

Judd was astounded. 'Do what? A woman? Is that her game? Take a letter, Miss Zamit. You've a pad and pencil handy?'

'Of course,' said Jenny, with a crisp little goody-goody smile.

'Here goes,' said Judd. 'Today's date, etc, etc. Dear Miss Zamit. You're fired.'

Judd's a serial sacker but, with Jenny fired, the week's quota of casualties was filled and I'd have left it there had not Young Woolford suggested later that I compromise Tankybums by getting him to say disrespectful things about Judd into a walkie-talkie.

His remarks would be picked up half a mile away, he said.

I found Tankybums and switched on the walkie-talkie. 'What's your opinion of Judd?' I said. 'Speak up.'

'He's a fine man,' said Tankybums. 'The best producer I've ever worked with.'

'Nonsense,' I said. 'Do you know what I think?'

'Yes,' said Tankybums. 'You think I don't know the walkie-talkie's on. Switch it off or I'll reveal that behind his back you referred to Judd as Fish Face.'

Young Woolford, looking triumphant, told me later that Judd wanted to see me in his office, where I was given the yellow card.

One more and I'll be packing my bags, so I'll have to keep my nose clean – may even have to show willing by attending Sparks's rave-up.

Pode and Popper Hit the Big Time

I hadn't imagined when writing here about my schoolfriends Pode and Popper (Pode dropped me, you may remember, and thereafter walked up to books with Popper) that either would crop up in my life again within a week or two.

Equally, I hadn't imagined, when, at the age of ten and dressed in plus-fours identical to my father's, I'd stood with him in line and, with a 12-bore twice my size, shot pheasants driven at us by dour retainers from a wood, that this unpleasant habit would prepare me for making documentary films – specifically, potting Brazilian transvestites in the Bois de Boulogne.

More of that shortly. First, I must admit that I've always quite enjoyed those obviously pornographic documentaries in which a small-time loser, asleep in his underwear, is held up to peak-time ridicule – is woken, in fact, before he has had a proper breakfast by burly VAT men running through his door, followed by keen young cameramen in gymshoes. Talk about insult on top of injury. Why, I've always wondered, doesn't he tell the television crew to push off out of it?

Now I know. Shooting *Root Into Europe* has taught me that documentary makers have rights that, though unwritten, are as clinching as those enshrined in Magna Carta; further, that scenes in documentaries are about as spontaneous as the self-regarding little skits in *Whose Line is It Anyway?* (a mock modest cry of dismay, an *artiste*'s hand flying to her mouth – 'that's *impossible*! I'll get you later, Clive!'); that they have, in fact, been carefully worked on, their participants' lines jotted down on cuffs, bits of scenery and so forth.

Here's what happens, more or less. A documentary maker on the up, a serious player in the game, approaches the VAT man and tells him he'd like to film a bust.

'Certainly, Sir,' the VAT man says. 'Any time, at your convenience. Personally, we prefer 4a.m. since at that hour the shock to chummy provides us with our biggest laugh, but the decision's yours, of course. Break a leg, duckie.'

Thereafter, small-time losers are auditioned, their agents consulted, the scene is written, lines are rehearsed, a release clause signed. Then the scene is shot and, if the director isn't satisfied, it's shot again – and again and again. Eventually, chummy gets five years and the director, if he's lucky, a Bafta award for the most realistic contribution to documentary making.

I may not be giving away a secret if I say that *Root Into Europe* contains a number of documentary scenes, nor if I admit that, because improvisation in my view never works, I had been apprehensive about these scenes before the shoot – indeed, had expressed my concern to Mark Chapman, our director.

'You have a very imperfect idea of how documentaries are

made,' he said. 'Each scene is carefully structured and rehearsed. We know exactly what we're doing.'

We certainly do, and no one more than Chapman himself, who brought to our preparations an awesome, unembarrassable intensity of purpose, never asking a ferry captain, a restaurateur or High Court judge whether he'd care to help us, but simply telling him that we intended to take over his practice for the day.

'I'll be brief, since I have another meeting soon,' he'd say. 'Here's what I plan to do. Oh, thank you – white with one sugar, please. Brown, of course. We have this very amusing scene in which George Cole as Root will call you a fool and suggest that you don't know beans about your business. It will mean, I'm afraid, that your restaurant/courtroom/cross-Channel ferry will have to close for the day. My secretary will be sending you your lines next week.'

Our finest hour, I think, came when we took over the police station in Paris's fifth *arrondissement*, thereafter obliging its captain to go on night patrol with George Cole and Chapman in the back seat of his car, and with two cameramen hanging from its boot and bonnet.

Rebuked by Chapman for failing to provide us with a filmable incident, and rightly embarrassed by the fact that the fifth was such a peaceable *arrondissement*, the captain later arranged for the central vice squad to bust the Bois de Boulogne on our behalf.

Chapman lined his cameras up and then instructed the vice squad's bull-necked chief to deploy his men like beaters, coming at tarts and punters from behind and driving them in our direction from under trees and out of bushes.

Ten minutes later a covey of fat men with their trousers around their knees ran full-tilt into our cameras, but Chapman wasn't satisfied. Some of the police had wielded their night sticks half-heartedly, he said, and the scene must be shot again. It was then that I spotted my old school friend Popper among a little knot of punters.

'See much of Pode these days?' I said.

'Not a lot,' he said. 'Excuse me. I think I'm in this scene. Can't keep the director waiting.'

Indeed not.

A Spanish New Man and Lardy English Types

I'm dead wood. I know this because Justin Judd, the producer of *Root Into Europe*, has told me so.

'You're dead wood,' he said on Monday, sidling up to me in a bar on Barcelona's Ramblas, where I was minding my own business while the others toiled.

I was a little surprised, not because I disagreed with him, but because he and I have recently been playing a complicated game of mouse and mouse, with neither of us inclined to show our claws. He naturally, wants me to fire myself so that he won't have to pay me any more, whereas I, obviously, would prefer him to wield the axe with, as a consequence, a nice untidy ending – a flurry of writs leading to an appearance in the chancery division of the High Court, where we would line up, I hope, in front of my pal Mr Justice Whitford who always finds for me, I'm glad to say, since he is temperamentally allergic to fat businessmen who try to use an expensively worded contract to separate an artist from his earnings.

That said, I don't want to be fired just yet. For one thing, the exhilarating spectacle of George Cole, as Root, and Pat Heywood, as Mrs Root, daily turning dross to gold before our eyes hasn't even begun to pall and, for another, I would like to survive at least until next Monday, when we are due to take our business to Ibiza.

Not that we'll ever get there. It's a miracle that, having left Barcelona on Tuesday, we arrived on Wednesday more or less intact in a little village in Aragon where, if such things existed still, we planned to shoot a superstitious turnout with the butcher's wife as the Virgin Mary, a slow march to slack drums, followed by the ceremonial spearing of a bull.

The fact is that an immobilizing rash of immorality has broken out, its cause being our Spanish location manager, Jordi Munoz – a perfectly adorable Catalan who has taken it upon himself to loosen up the lardy, heavy-footed, rather common English types with whom – to his obvious dismay – he has suddenly been thrown into such disagreeable proximity.

131

'Hallo,' he says, 'I'm Jordi,' and then he massages you deeply, and with welcome intimacy, between the shoulder blades, after which he asks you if you'd like to see his house.

He's only being polite, of course. He's a Spanish new man, as unlike your macho old-time *hombre* with a frozen chicken down his tights as it's possible to be; he would, if you insulted his sister, still ask you if you'd like to see his house. But everyone has fallen for his charm – even the girls, which surprises me since girls don't usually go for this sort of stuff. The girls' knees knock like castanets and their normally keen features lose definition and melt away like the lines of a pavement portrait in the rain, only to reassemble into that ecstatic, oddly idiotic look more usually associated with matrons at a Tom Jones concert.

Then there are the late night phone calls. I know about these because I've been getting them. What the girls haven't yet twigged is that, if you want to dial from room to room in our hotel, you have to add a 3 to the number you want. Jordi is in room 9 and I'm in room 39. Last night my phone rang just as I'd got off to sleep.

'Do anything you like to me, you mad Spanish brute,' a voice urgently implored me. 'Clamp me to the bedpost with your Barcelona football supporter's club tie. Let me lock my downy, sunkissed thighs around your . . .' I'll not say who it was, merely who it wasn't. It wasn't Luke Schiller, my favourite, who has recently broken up with his beloved, Poppy, and is quietly grieving still. Nor was it my ex-favourite, Catey Sexton, who, after a long affair, has recently broken up with herself. Nor, I'm glad to say, was it Mrs Marvin from Norwich who, as the wife of my pal Gary Marvin, Wykeham Professor of Bulls at the University of East Anglia, is with us to advise on superstitious festivals and so forth.

And it's just as well she has. We lined our cameras up today and asked the locals where the bull was.

'What bull?' they asked.

'Leave this to me,' said Mrs Marvin, who is really Carmen Dominguez Cobos from Seville. 'I'll persuade the mayor to get us a bull. I'm very attractive to dirty old mans.'

'I'm a dirty old mans,' I said.

'You're dead wood,' said Mrs Marvin.

Be that as it may, the mayor laid on a bull which, disappointingly, turned out to be as much of a new man as our location manager, Jordi Munoz. It trotted into the square and sat down, quite ignoring the young men who (coached by us, since they had never done anything so daft) attempted to enrage it by hanging from lamp-posts and waving copies of *El Pais* above their heads. And there it still might be, had not Mrs Marvin from Norwich whacked it on the backside and chased it towards our waiting cameras.

'It's a new man,' I said to Jordi Munoz. 'If you insulted its sister, it would ask you if you would like to see its house.'

'Better a new man than dead wood,' he said.

Word travels fast in a small company.

My Baby's Long in Glaxo

Last week, you may remember, Justin Judd, the producer of *Root Into Europe*, described me as dead wood. This week I'm back in production – more accurately, reclining on a beach in Ibiza with my literary agent, Alison – whereas he has been hospitalized by an extra. It's a funny old world indeed.

The incident took place in Barcelona. A tiny shoeshine man, almost a dwarf, having performed well all day, beckoned Judd over to say farewell. Judd, who is unnaturally tall, stooped low, almost doubled over out of courtesy. When they were nose to nose, the shoeshine man nutted him, their heads meeting with the satisfactory thwack of two conkers at a prep school.

'Damn me,' said Judd, and then he went down like a sack of meal. We all had a good laugh, Judd was stretchered to the clinic and I, as associate producer, naturally inherited his duties, not to say the purse strings – the latter being handed over with some show of reluctance, I thought, by Mark Chapman, our director.

'You have nothing to worry about,' I said. 'I'm an excellent businessman, as anyone will tell you. I failed as a theatrical producer only because I had appalling taste. The company's per diems are secure with me. I'll need a moneybelt and an adequate float, of course.'

I was particularly keen to perform my duties well, in fact since Ibiza was next on the agenda and only I, it seemed to me, could find a suitable replacement for Tanit the Island God, whose annual two-week break clashed, we'd just discovered, with our shooting schedule. I didn't want one of my colleagues – good eggs in the normal run of things but likely under stress to talk about motor cars and money, to give the impression that their ideas had been designed by the same chap as had done their writing paper and bathroom taps – to scare the daylights out of every resting black man on the island.

It was with some disappointment, then, that I discovered at lunchtime on our first day that Chapman had already invited a beautiful Indian from Brazil called Kevin – a dancer trained in the Isadora Duncan school, now fashioning croissants in a local bakery – to play the part of Tanit.

I admitted, ungrudgingly I hope, that Kevin seemed ideal and then returned to the beach where my literary agent, Alison, was reading the *Financial Times*. She looked so sweetly serious that I was forced to make one of my little speeches.

'You break my heart,' I said. 'I'm awash with love. You combine such sweetness of nature and loveliness . . .'

'I can't be bothered with all that stuff while I'm checking my stocks and shares,' she said. 'I'm long in Glaxo. I'll have to ring my broker.'

I was crushed, frankly, felt the need suddenly for a mood-altering substance and said as much to Alison.

'Do you know where to get it?' she said.

'No problem,' I said. 'According to the Sunday tabloids, you can't stand around for two minutes in Ibiza town without some fiend offering you a deal.' I tapped my producer's moneybelt. 'And for once we're adequately capitalized.'

That evening we positioned ourselves appropriately and within minutes six fiends had sidled up to us – but they turned out to be tabloid journalists wanting to buy stuff from me. Then our luck changed. I winked at a gypsy and he winked back, so I gave him a lot of money and he gave me a bag of wood shavings.

'Why didn't you protest?' said Alison.

'The sprat to catch the mackerel,' I explained. 'You've got to encourage these chaps. And you must admit the deal was good. This bag must weigh at least two ounces.' Then I gave the gypsy a lot more money, but had to agree with Alison – when it seemed I might be running out of sprats – that the system wasn't working. I'd have packed it in had not Kevin the croissantier joined us at that moment.

'Hi,' he said. 'I'd like to thank you for the break you've given me. I'm keen to study modern dance in Cuba and the fee will go towards my air fare. I'm really looking forward to tomorrow's filming.'

'Never mind that,' I said. 'I'm after something with a little more kick to it than wood shavings, if you take my drift. Can you help?'

'Of course,' said Kevin the croissantier. 'And if you can advance me a thousand pounds I can get it for nothing. You take what you want and I'll sell the rest at a profit which I'll share with you.'

That seemed sensible. I emptied the moneybelt and off he went.

'It would be amusing,' said Alison, 'if you'd lost the crew's per diems and, more seriously, Tanit the Island God's replacement. I expect he's on his way to Cuba.'

'No chance,' I said. 'I'm an excellent judge of character.'

I don't have to go on, you'll be way ahead of me. Half an hour later Kevin the croissantier returned with the goods, my initial investment and £200 which represented my share of the profit – but the stuff had been heavily cut. It was OK, but I'll be more careful next time.

When in Rome, Pay the Mafia

The trouble with old people these days is they think they know it all. In fact they're doing well if they can remember their own names. The brain goes before the legs which is why you can't do mathematics or play chess after the age of twenty-five – certainly, unlike Mark Chapman, I didn't know that the net probable benefit of everyone giving money to the Mafia can be expressed as $V = p1(a-f(1)) + p2(2a-f(2)) + \ldots pn(na-f(n))$.

If only the old knew and the young could, is more to the

point; the young for their part being as spirited as sponges, planning sophisticated repayment schemes in their terraced, mortgaged houses when they should be out there turning somersaults.

In a nutshell, the little someone knew when he was twenty will have been forgotten by the time he's fifty – not that this applies to me. I didn't know anything in the first place, except more than anyone else about American football (certainly, more than the 49ers' coach who, in the close season, allowed Ronnie Lott to move to the LA Raiders) and the names, oddly, of every Wimbledon champion since 1947, even that of Stan Smith. ('One of nature's gentleman, Dan. When Stan played, whatever the result, tennis was the winner,' and that's another thing I've never understood.)

All my life, then, I've known too little and, suddenly, I know too much. Not that I can tell you what I know – or whom I learnt it from. All I can say is that the *Root Into Europe* shoot has moved to Italy and that on Monday in Rome – under plain cover and at a location so secret that we still don't know where it was – Mark Chapman and I met one of the few investigating magistrates honest and brave enough to carry on the fight against the Mafia.

Flanked by bodyguards whom he didn't trust ('I trust no one,' he said, 'least of all the men who appointed me'– a disconcerting moment, I can tell you), he gave us the names of the Mafia bosses who control everything in London, the hotels, wine bars, banks and other businesses they own, and where they live – Woking, for the most part, as it happens, and that struck me as odd since Woking is neither here nor there, I've always thought.

He also told us, embarrassingly, of Scotland Yard's patronizing English disbelief when it was pointed out to them that the Mafia was comfortably in place in London. Informed that Luciano Leggio (boss of the Corleonesi family – the winning factor in the war of '81) had sent the Caruana brothers and Francesco Di Carlo to London to organize the distribution of hard drugs in the UK, Commander Colin Hewitt, head of Scotland Yard's Drug Intelligence Unit, said: 'We have no Mafia problem here in London.' ('Thank you, Salvatore, but I think we'd have noticed if a few fat men in baggy trousers were running around Soho with their banjo cases.')

'I have three kinds of enemy,' the investigating magistrate said. 'The dons who control everything from Sicily; the men in suits – the politicians, lawyers and bankers – who do their bidding; and people like yourselves who, through ignorance or greed, buy shares in Mafia-owned companies and check their progress in the City pages of the *Daily Telegraph*, or, worse, make silly documentary films that glamorize the problem.'

Mark Chapman, whose hold on the moral high ground is more secure than that of anyone I know, took exception to the last part of this, at least. 'For one thing,' he said, 'I wouldn't be seen dead reading the *Daily Telegraph*.

'And for another, I wouldn't put a penny into the Mafia's coffers. I'd tell them to push off.'

The next day we paid up instantly when a man built like a billiard ball told us that, as we planned to film in rather a rough part of Rome, we'd be advised to take out an insurance policy with his uncle.

'That's a bit of a contradiction,' I said.

'Not in any formal sense,' said Chapman. 'A theory isn't refuted by one's failure to act on its consequences.'

'What if everyone paid the Mafia?' I said.

'That's another mistake,' young Chapman said. 'The "what if everyone" argument isn't as clinching as you'd wish. It considers each person as confronted with the choice of, say, either giving money to the Mafia or of not doing so. However, there is a third possibility, which is that each person should, with the aid of a randomizing device, such as a dice, award himself a certain probability of giving money to the Mafia.

'Were we to allot numerical values to the private benefit of giving money to the Mafia and the public harm done by one, two, three, etc persons doing so, we could work out a value of the probability that each reasonable utilitarian should give himself. Suppose that 'p' is the probability that each person will give money to the Mafia. Let these probabilities be $p1, p2 \ldots pn$. Then the total net probable benefit of giving money to the Mafia can be expressed as $V = p1(a-f(1)) + p2(2a-f(2)) + \ldots pn(na-f(n))$.

That's another thing I'd quite forgotten, if I ever knew it.

Ronnie Kray Prefers Jimmy Tarbuck

I have mentioned before, I think, that the head of some department at the BBC once gave me a beefy lecture on the art of situation comedy and then, since *Root Into Europe* was under discussion, brought up the subject of casting.

'What about Root?' he said. 'Nigel Havers, do you think?'

Should Ronnie Kray – who once urgently advised me to dismiss Nicol Williamson from a West End entertainment and replace him with Jimmy Tarbuck – ever be released, he could take over from this chap at the BBC without anyone noticing the change.

I wouldn't, in the normal run of things, front up to Ronnie Kray, but one evening in 1964 I was obliged to do just that since, at the time, I was mounting a musical with my Barclaycard, which had temporarily fallen into Mr Kray's possession.

With Mrs Mouse, Birmingham Paul and Birmingham Paul's bodyguard, Winston – a large, scholarly-looking man who spoke in a sinister, asthmatic whisper (the result, I believe, of an old gangland war wound to the windpipe) – I had gone one evening, though I can't imagine why, to Verdi's Grey Topper, a nightclub in Covent Garden.

I hadn't expected any bother, nor would I have been concerned if bother had cropped up. Some months earlier a promoter, who was about to mount a pop concert in a famously unpleasant part of Birmingham, had asked me to advise him on security. I'd put the matter in the hands of Birmingham Paul who had then said that he'd given the job to Winston.

'Just Winston?' I'd asked.

'Winston,' Birmingham Paul had said, 'is more than a match for a few hundred Birmingham hooligans.'

I was sitting contentedly at Verdi's Grey Topper, then, when a fight broke out on the dance floor. It seemed to be in slow motion, as in a western. Large men in Cecil Gee suits, a size too small, fisted pillars sailed head first into pyramids of bottles. A comically small waiter was hit on the nose, spun through 360 degrees and was hit on the nose again. Mr Verdi appealed for order, had his hat knocked off, the band played on.

I was enjoying myself, didn't for some time realize that the fight was real. It was Winston, in fact, who tipped us off.

'It's the twins,' he croaked, having more respect for Ronnie and Reggie, it seemed, than for a few hundred Birmingham yobs in a rented discotheque. 'We'd better get out.'

I called for the bill, paid with my Barclaycard, made for the exit. Then I realized that I had left my Barclaycard behind. I had plans, as I said, to mount a musical with my Barclaycard – *Nights at the Comedy*, starring Nicol Williamson, Mrs Shufflewick and Queenie Watts – so there was nothing for it but to return to our table where Ronnie Kray was now sitting, holding my Barclaycard.

'That's mine,' I said – an odd thing to do, but such was the need for credit when mounting musicals. 'I'm in showbusiness, you understand. *Nights at the Comedy*, starring Nicol Williamson.'

'A difficult *artiste* from all I hear,' said Ronnie. 'Lose him and get the new boy Tarbuck, that's my advice.'

I tell this story now to demonstrate the extraordinary lengths to which an impresario, gripped by some duff fantasy, will go to see it realized on stage; further, to educate the surprisingly large number of people who, since I revealed last week that I and my colleagues on *Root Into Europe* had paid the Mafia to allow us to film peaceably in Rome, have criticised us for doing so.

Our critics fail to understand that we showbiz types – not least directors of documentary films – allow *nothing* to stand between us and our arrangements, refuse to recognize, in fact – though I have remarked on the phenomenon often enough – the sheer weight of our intentions.

We are like a small boy who, given a conjuring set for Christmas, thereafter sits his parents down, together with the neighbours and the neighbours' cat, and compels them to watch helplessly while he performs his tricks.

Irritated that our filming was temporarily held up, we have shaken old ladies awake and rudely told them to doze elsewhere; we have trapped fifty schoolgirls in a restaurant and refused to let them use the lavatory ('Do what?! We're trying to make a film!'); we have pointed cross-channel ferries in the wrong direction and instructed the French police to humiliate every tart and punter in the Bois de Boulogne. Were we to be thwarted at the final hurdle by a dapper Roman whose demands anyway were entirely reasonable – merely that six of his girlfriends appear as extras, albeit in a scene in which no extras were required?

'What do you think of it so far?' I asked him during a break.

'*Ha considerato Nigel Havers per il ruolo di Root?*' he asked.

I didn't feel inclined to listen. *Nights at the Comedy* had opened in 1964 with Jimmy Tarbuck in place of Nicol Williamson and had flopped horribly two weeks later.

I Buy a Club in Gerrard Street

I was once quoting Auden to Dawn Upstairs – not necessarily a rewarding thing to do – specifically the bit about prostitutes and opera singers surviving revolutions.

'Joan Sutherland,' I said.

'Here,' said Dawn Upstairs. 'Is that Big Joan from Chelsea Cloisters?'

'She's an opera singer,' I said.

'Second string to her bow,' said Dawn Upstairs. 'You should acquire one of them.'

I have since then striven diligently to achieve this end but had not, until this week, succeeded. Nor is a second string to my bow my only recent triumph; I have, too, become a member of the Mafia. I haven't made my bones, been to the mattresses or any of that stuff, but I'm deeply involved, I think. This latter circumstance is closely connected with the former, but more of that in due course. Suffice to say that neither state of affairs has arrived too soon. The fact is that with only two weeks to go on the *Root Into Europe* shoot, relations between myself and my senior colleagues on the enterprise (Mark Chapman, the director, and the producer, Justin Judd) have broken down completely, though whose fault this is I'm not quite sure. Probably it's 50–50. That is to say, it's 50 per cent Mark Chapman's fault and 50 per cent Justin Judd's.

No, no – that's a joke, and not a very good one. The truth, of course, is entirely otherwise. All the blame, as anyone on the shoot will tell you, must be attributed to Justin Judd – and that's a joke too, the standard of this and the previous one explaining, perhaps, why I have been phased out as writer of the show, my duties having been taken over by the assistant producer, Jeremy Lovering.

What tipped me off to this was a growing awareness that young Lovering who, previously, had been keenly in the thick of it, perched on Chapman's shoulder and able, without blushing, to parrot the embarrassing catchphrases of chaps with cameras in the offing ('As quick as you like!', 'Happiness, people?', 'It's a wrap folks, if the gate's clean') was being phased out too, marginalized at least, and was spending more and more time sitting on the pavement next to me, jotting down stuff in an exercise book while the others played elsewhere. I assumed at first that he was putting the finishing touches to his novel, but he soon straightened me out on that.

'When *you* were the writer of the show,' he said, 'did you find that you were being pushed more and more to one side, that you were being taken less seriously than the grip's assistant?'

'Certainly,' I said. 'Film people, with their half-witted notions about images on a screen and so forth, dislike writers intensely – it's been well documented in many books. Still, it must be exciting for you hearing a comedy actor of genius like George Cole speaking your lines.'

'When they *are* my lines,' said Lovering unhappily. 'Chapman blue-pencils my stuff without so much as a by my leave and seeks improvements from anyone who happens to be passing by. Waiters. Mad women with trolleys. Street derelicts. Even Justin Judd. Next time I'll direct the thing myself. May I resort to an analogy?'

'By all means.'

'It's as if one's home has been taken over by a group of people who, for reasons which aren't entirely clear, have every right to be there. They rearrange your furniture, cut down the roses in your garden, paint the drawing-room. As they take over the more comfortable quarters, you find yourself sleeping in the attic. Some are polite, others don't know who you are or why you're there. Eventually you have to leave.'

'It must be ghastly,' I said. 'Tell me something, however. What gave you the idea for Root and how did you think of the name? Henry Root seems perfect.'

'What crap questions,' said Lovering. 'You sound like a disc jockey on a provincial chat show. Excuse me, I've got to join young Woolford in the baggage van.'

It occurred to me that Lovering, as writer of the show, will let us all down badly when he's required to publicize it, sulkily refusing to answer perfectly reasonable questions put to him by Wogan, Aspel, Hunniford and so forth. I should care, however. Shortly after our conversation my pal the local Mafia man, Emilio Scarlatti (christened Rat Face 'The Fink' Lucchese, later changed by deed poll), made me an offer I couldn't refuse.

'You need a second string to your bow,' he said. 'My associates and I are prepared to sell you a club in Gerrard Street. It's going for a song, in spite of the fact that the Princess of Wales and her young friends visit it almost every night.'

I liked the sound of that and was on to my London lawyer in a brace of shakes, instructing him to sell a couple of my houses to raise the purchase price.

Never mind *Root Into Europe*, I can hardly wait for my return to London on the 21st when I'll be able to inspect my property and take up my position on the door. A second string to my bow indeed.

The Princess of Wales, Jillypoo and Ted the Head

Last week, you may remember, I described how I had been phased out as the writer of *Root Into Europe*, my duties – such as they were – being taken over by Jeremy Lovering, the assistant producer.

Since then, a surprisingly large number of people have written in, sympathizing with me over what they judged had been somewhat insensitive behaviour on Lovering's part. On the shoot, too, I was treated for an embarrassing day or two like some fragile old party who might have bruised.

142

In Baden Baden, where we were when the piece appeared, Pat Heywood helped me to load the baggage van, and Julia Hancock, who has been my real favourite all along, bought me a nectarine which 'Toddy' Zamit immediately ate. ('Toddy' is a little distracted at the moment because her team, the Cincinnati Bengals, are 0 and 7 – and what, apart from the boastful and self-pitying Welsh getting stuffed by a country with a population the size of Neasden's, only fifteen of whom play rugger, could be funnier than that?)

Anyway, I had not at all intended to give the impression that Lovering's behaviour had been gauche or clumsy. Lovering, as I've said many times before, is as spirited as a person twice his age, and I like to think that I, more than anyone else, have encouraged him to grab the ball and jink with it nimbly to the try-line. If, in the process, a fat, gasping prop finds himself face down in the mud, so what?

Lovering's behaviour, it seems to me, was no more careless than that of my Uncle Fred who, when my father was dying, flew down from Glasgow to visit him in hospital, already wearing his funeral suit. There was no time for the niceties, Uncle Fred had a plane to catch, he was on his way. So, too, is Lovering. Old guns, young Turks, pass the baton and so forth.

Further, as I said last week, I now have this second string to my bow – a half share in the Toucan Club in Gerrard Street, purchased from the family man in Rome, my pal Emilio 'The Fink' Scarlatti – and Lovering's disgraceful behaviour provided me with an opportunity to walk out in a sulk, to return to London and inspect my property.

The fact is, I hadn't much enjoyed the shoot; more accurately, I hadn't enjoyed it at all. What had surprised me most, I think, was that everyone else involved seemed to look on it as work – evidence of this being that once a week we were given a day off.

The trick, as I see it, is to get paid for what you do anyway and, if you can't get that organized, you might as well sit on a beach with corks in your hat. Either way, what's the point of a day off? I've never done a day's work in my life (except when I inadvertently did the same day twice at Ogilvy & Mather), and, equally, have never had a day off.

There had, too, been a telling incident in Paris during the first week of the shoot. A street drunk, with one leg and a parrot on his shoulder, kept wandering into the action, giving his opinion on how the scene might be better directed and offering Mark Chapman a swig from his bottle of red wine. Chapman finally blew up with an exasperated 'not while I'm *working*!', obviously expecting 'working' to have the effect on the drunk of garlic on a vampire. The drunk rocked with laughter, and so did I. Why, I wondered, hadn't Chapman taken a swig or, at least, said 'not while I'm amusing myself making silly movies'? This isn't for me, I thought.

My attitude, of course, has required me to be pretty quick on my feet, keeping one eye cocked for opportunities and going into business with others who have never done a day's work – like my pal Emilio 'The Fink' Scarlatti and his cousin, my partner in the Toucan Club, John 'Baby Face' Scarlatti, whom I visited within hours of flying back to London.

The club's doing well, I'm glad to say, and Baby Face, with whom I hit it off immediately, is keen to keep it as it is – which, depressingly, is a sort of up-market version of the Groucho. I had imagined something a touch more *louche*, the sort of place where Jillypoo, Black Simone and Ted the Head would feel at home, and I said as much to Baby Face.

'But the Princess of Wales is a member,' he said.

'I can't imagine why,' I said.

'She was introduced by her connections in the world of fashion,' Baby Face said. 'Wayne Sleep, Bert Oldfield, Jasper Carrott and so forth. Movers and shakers.'

'Precisely the kind of people I'm trying to avoid,' I said. 'The trick is to run a club you'd want to join yourself.'

'What sort of club is that?'

'There's no such thing,' I said. 'I wouldn't be seen dead in a club. Not that that need trouble you. I wouldn't be seen dead in a theatre, but I was happy once to be an impresario.'

'How did that go?'

'A complete cock-up.'

'I'm a trifle worried,' said Baby Face. 'When does Jeremy Lovering get back to London? I greatly admired his award-winning piece in this month's *Elle*.'

I could have problems here, I think.

144

S and M is Just the Thing

In spite of my piece last week, in which I sought publicly to excuse young Lovering for the robust way in which he had removed me from my position as writer of *Root Into Europe* (not unlike Micky Skinner's second-half, blind-side tackle on the French No 8, Marc Cécillon – and what, apart from Ronnie Lott's sudden demolition job on the Giants' neurotic, God-fearing tight end, Mark Bavaro, in last season's play-off game at Candlestick Park, could have been more exhilarating than that?), letters have continued to pour in criticizing Lovering for what readers insist on seeing as loutish, even unconscionable behaviour.

Some – vulgarly, in my opinion – go so far as to use the incident against Germaine Greer, seeking to show that post-menopausal men must expect to undergo the same humiliations as are visited, it seems, on women. I can't see it – or, rather, I can see it, but prefer to regard what happened to me, and must happen to all of us as we get older, as a kind of natural rough justice, not as an occasion for self-pity.

What goes round comes round, as my friend Dawn Upstairs insists on saying after a brief working holiday in California; and the atrocities I committed in my twenties against anyone who had the misfortune to be more than forty certainly make Lovering's behaviour towards me seem positively kind.

I have written before, I believe, of the way I treated my father who spent his last years singing bleak Scottish laments in a dark room in Sunningdale, while various Indian poets and I drank his gin and sneered at him because he didn't understand.

I have described, too, I think, the circumstances by which I became a theatrical producer – on a whim, purchasing such goodwill as still accrued to Jack Waller, an old-time impresario who had presented *No, No, Nanette* and other successful entertainments – but may not have admitted that I also purchased his seventy-three-year-old general manager, Bert Leywood, who had once been half of a novelty dance duo, Albert Woodley and Ivy.

He was a sweet old man but I treated him with vicious insolence. Irritated by his habit – affectionately meant, I'm sure – of referring to me as 'the boy', I first tried to blast him out and,

145

when this didn't work, I embarked on a campaign of methodical slow torture, moving him into smaller and smaller offices until he and his mementoes of happier days ended up in a broom cupboard in the hall.

Every morning he struggled up from Worthing on the train, thereafter, and uncomplainingly, taking up his position in the cupboard where first he'd ring up a pal of his who had once produced *The Amorous Prawn* starring 'Boo' Laye, and then he'd doze for the rest of the day, recalling times, perhaps, when he hadn't been so lonely, when he and his beloved Ivy had sat together in their Worthing garden and everything had been all right.

One day, when *Beyond the Fringe* was on its try-out tour in Brighton, he received an urgent message in his cupboard that my boy Charlie, aged two, had knocked a kettle of hot water over himself, and, judging that he should break this news to me face to face, he caught the train to Brighton and hurried, as fast as his old legs would carry him, to the Theatre Royal.

Unaware that there was a matinée in progress, he stumbled on to the stage, crying 'Where's the boy, where's the boy?' in the middle of some smart skit or other. The audience roared with laughter and this embarrassed him so much that he fell over a piece of scenery and sustained a nasty nosebleed. I had a good laugh, too, and for all I know he may still be there.

So – how do I pull the rug from under Baby Face Scarlatti, my partner in the Toucan Club?

The old poop can't be more than fifty-one but he's as much fun as a twenty-two-year-old who has just negotiated his first index-linked pension plan, and advice from you on how I can remove him would be a jolly sight more useful than a load of sentimental guff about Lovering's foul behaviour.

It's an absurd state of affairs. When I'm on the door I let in people you and I would want to meet but, when I hop into Gerrard Street for a curry, Baby Face throws them out and lets in inebriated old theatricals who must have found the Groucho Club a little too exciting.

In one bizarre, rotating incident, I refused entry to the gifted crooner Jimmy Somerville, mistaking him for Ian Hislop. Twenty minutes later I went off duty and Baby Face turned Hislop away, thinking he was Jimmy Somerville.

146

Never mind. Not all your letters have been silly. A Miss Ruth Marks of the International Mackintosh Society wants to book the club for an evening of S and M, and since I am persuaded – by the fashion pages of the *Independent*, no less – that S and M is just the thing, I ran her request past Baby Face.

The silly old fool thinks that S and M stands for sausage and mash and is preparing a gala night for pensioners.

Six Skinny Women from the Groucho Club

Tories, and others to the right of centre, famously lack a sense of humour, of course, but I was a little surprised to hear that 14,000 readers cancelled their subscriptions to the *Daily Telegraph* following a joke last week by Auberon Waugh.

You don't read the *Telegraph*, I imagine, so you'll be unaware that Mr Waugh wrote with approval of the fact that, in line with a Euro-ruling by the excellent Jacques Delors, the Queen Mother's role was to be reduced and rendered henceforth, here and on the Euro-stage, by old Queen Juliana of the Netherlands.

It wasn't Mr Waugh's joke that enraged his readers, since they were not aware that a joke had been attempted; they cancelled their subscriptions and moved in their middle-market thousands to the more reliable *Daily Mail* because Mr Waugh expressed his satisfaction with Delors's initiative.

And they'll be uncomfortable with the *Mail*, too, I think, if the reaction to Nigel Dempster's brilliant recent joke, involving Pamella Bordes and Richard Ingrams, is anything to go by. Mr Dempster, you may remember, suggested that this unlikely couple had enjoyed what Mr Ingrams would call – and undoubtedly consider – a dirty weekend in Brighton, and this was swallowed whole not only by readers of the *Daily Mail* but by Ingrams, too, who felt obliged to publish a load of horse feathers, insisting he himself had been Dempster's informant. I have not been able to discover Miss Bordes's reaction to being publicly, and so unflatteringly, yoked, but Mr Dempster is a conscientious reporter and we can assume, I think, that he would have secured Miss Bordes's collusion in advance.

Coincidentally, my friend Wallace Arnold told me this week of his relief at joining the *Independent on Sunday* from the right-wing *Spectator* where neither his editor nor his readers understood that his column was a joke, and in whose letter pages, therefore, the former consistently published uncomprehending nonsense from the latter.

'After the *Spectator*,' Mr Arnold told me over a disgusting lunch (he is also a restaurant critic, so one lunches with him without any particular expectation of a decent meal) 'working for the *Independent* is like drinking an iced tumblerful of lovingly squeezed fresh lemons on a muggy English afternoon in Essex.'

My feelings precisely. On the rare occasions I construct a joke – publishing the same column five times in a row, for instance, as I did recently in a hopeful parody of Jeffrey Bernard's mature style, and in which I skittishly pretended I'd become an alcoholic – *Independent* readers understand that a joke has been attempted and politely allow the thing to pass. They don't submit indignant letters asking what I'm on about, nor do they send in the names and addresses of barmy self-help groups and rehabilitation clinics.

Equally, if I genuinely seek readers' help, they come up trumps. The response to my request last week for assistance in the matter of the Toucan Club, and for advice on how to pull the rug from under my partner, has been overwhelming.

Overwhelming, but, alas, entirely useless. I can't, for instance, lock him up in the broom cupboard in the hall in the way that I locked up old Bert Leywood, a previous partner of mine, because we haven't got a broom cupboard; nor, come to that, have we got a hall – you just pile up the stairs and hope for the best.

Further, I haven't got a partner any more; more accurately, I have a partner, but a different one. No sooner had the first one gone on holiday than another one pitched up, and he's worse than the previous one. Between you and me, I think he's one of *those* – by which I mean a whinnying old actor with the literary tastes of a semi-educated country curate.

On Monday, in an attempt to raise the tone, I'd persuaded my friend Terence Blacker to cancel his usual gig at the Dominas with Attitude Club in the Tottenham Court Road, to wear

148

trousers by Jean Paul Gaultier and sing stuff to his own accompaniment while sitting astride a motor-bicycle in our upstairs room.

By the time I arrived, however, my new partner had dismissed Blacker and had, in his place, invited Jeremy Lovering to field questions put to him by six skinny women from the Groucho Club (the same six plonkers, incidentally, who this week, incredibly, awarded The Hooker Prize – a tiny prophylactic, amusingly described as the world's smallest condom – to Martin Amis for services to male chauvinism). There has been some ill-feeling between me and Lovering, you may remember, since he took over my writer's duties on *Root Into Europe*.

'Tell me, Mr Lovering,' said one of the wallies from the Groucho Club, 'to what extent are *you* Henry Root? Can you, through him, express right-wing views of which you'd otherwise be ashamed?'

'What a crap question,' Lovering said. 'I'll be off now.'

Advice from you on how I can get rid of my new partner and, once and for all, discredit Lovering, would be extremely welcome.

Drugs and Protection? We Tried That

In my circle it's considered common to ask people what they do for a living, even when you've known them half your life. I've scarcely recovered, in fact, from my literary agent Alison's look of icy dismay when curiosity got the better of me one day and I asked her what sort of business, if any, her previous young man (with whom she'd lived for three years) happened to have been in.

'I haven't the faintest idea,' she said. 'I never asked.'

We can all make prats of ourselves, but I felt as silly as Jeffrey Archer must have felt when he pitched up on the Saturday of Royal Ascot week in a morning coat and topper; or as keen that the ground should open up in front of me as Julie Burchill must have been when, on being introduced to Martin Amis at a literary do at the Polish Club, she asked him to what extent (she was seized by panic, we can assume) he thought his syntax had been affected by his height.

My greatest *faux pas* in this department occurred, however, at one of Dopey Linda's musical evenings in Queen's Gate where I naturally gravitated towards another well behaved old party in a suit whom I took to be an accountant or something of the sort. We hit it off so well that, after a while, I asked him whether the books were balancing out all right, or something chatty along those lines, whereupon he gave me a funny look and sidled off to talk to someone else.

I was a little disconcerted, even more so when I was advised, for safety's sake, to leave the party. My new pal, I was told, happened to be Joe 'Crazy Horse' Wilkins, the extortioner and nightclub boss who, in the general run of things, carried a gun when visiting the launderette and didn't take kindly to questions about his source of income.

Since then I've been more careful – hadn't, indeed, until this week asked my new partner in the Toucan Club what trade he usually followed. Last Friday, however, having stared at him silently all week as we went about our business, I gave in to natural curiosity.

'Don't I know you?' I said.

He looked at me rather guardedly, which was reasonable, I suppose.

'Possibly,' he said.

'Your face is very familiar,' I said. 'I'm sure I've seen you somewhere before.'

'I should certainly hope so,' he said, tossing his head and arranging his mouth in a Page Three pout. 'I've been on television quite a lot.'

It was worse than I feared. Not only did he look like an actor, he was an actor – this circumstance accounting, no doubt, for our increasingly disreputable clientele. It's no longer, frankly, just skinny jumped-up publishing women from the Groucho, crossing their legs recklessly and talking turkey, but middle-aged men, too, who look like Nigel Havers, keen young independents with a development up their sleeves and corporate video types from Charlotte Street.

150

When we're open the Wigmore Club must be as empty as Old Mother Hubbard's cupboard. Neither the Princess of Wales nor Dan Farson will come any more; an evening in our upstairs room must be worse than being stuck for an hour with John Sessions; Keith Floyd walked out last week because he found the prevailing tone a little too facetious; and compared to an average conversation among our members, Rumpole of the Bailey's laborious locutions would seem positively lively.

I was so distraught that I took the unusual step of seeking the advice of my temporary literary agent, Cat Ledger.

'I hope you don't want to talk about your work,' she said.

I reassured her on that point and she agreed to meet me at the club on Tuesday.

'This is delightful,' she said, scanning the room for contracts. 'But it is Soho. What about drug users and protection?'

'No good,' I said. 'Users won't mix with drinkers. They'd rather sit peaceably at home than be pinned against the wall by raconteurs who later vomit on their shoes.'

'Is that Rosie Cheetham over there?' Ledger said. 'We'll not want to be seen with her.'

'Never mind Rosie Cheetham,' I said. 'As for protection, I did consider it – hopping into the Chinese restaurant next door and asking for a monkey on account – but when I was last in the West End, running the Establishment with Raymond Nash, we found that the police had always put in their demand ahead of us. Nash, who could carry his own body weight in gold, decided to smuggle a ton of the stuff to Japan. He was arrested when he sat down in Tokyo airport and the sofa collapsed under him.'

'Well, I feel quite at home,' Ledger said. 'Oh look – there's Gail Rebuck. Excuse me.'

I cheered up later when I found myself talking to a very nice woman who seemed far too bright to be a member. I told her my name, adding, I don't know why, that I was a journalist.

'What do you do?' I said.

'I edit the features pages of the *Independent*,' she said. 'You must let me see your stuff some time.'

Never ask someone what they do for a living.

Boots, Maxwell and Telephonic Terrorism

My friend Boots has been broken by the system. I've not mentioned Boots before, I think, and I wouldn't mention her now had not the sad death of Robert Maxwell naturally made one focus on the endlessly fascinating question of how out of the ordinary you can be without the men in white coats taking you away.

For one distinguished commentator the tragedy brought to mind Chapter 54 of Thomas à Kempis's *The Imitation of Christ* ('Nature has regard to temporal things, rejoices at earthly gain, is troubled at losses . . .') – I'm referring here to Maxwell's death, not to the system's crushing of my friend Boots – and Samuel Johnson's *The Vanity of Human Wishes* ('Maxwell did seem to have "a frame of adamant" if not quite "a soul of fire", one could fairly say that "No dangers fright him and no labours tire."')

I thought he was as mad as a March hare. On one occasion in his office he told me about his technique on the telephone which he described as 'telephone terrorism'.

'Say what you want to say,' Maxwell told me, 'and then put the receiver down. Remember that. Make your point and down with the phone. It always works.'

Completely barking. Boots, by contrast, is as sane as you and me – was until recently, at least. I've never been sure what Boots does for a living (as I explained last week, it's considered common in my circle to ask people how they make ends meet), but I imagine she's in the furniture business; either that or she's a burglar.

I first met her a few years ago when she knocked on my door one day with her partner Clogs, banged round my apartment for a while – looking in wardrobes, opening and closing drawers, taking pictures off the wall and so forth – and then said: 'Glad to see someone isn't bothering to keep up with the Joneses. Two hundred pounds the lot.'

I agreed and we became friends. She was great fun, always carried a bankroll the size of a breeze block in her bag and obviously had her faculties intact, never more so than when she came to tea a month ago – a circumstance made all the more remarkable by the fact that Clogs had just hit her over the head with a sockful of wet cement.

Contracted by a fashion house to move a rail of clothes from one high street location to another, she and Clogs had decided to stage a mugging. For realism's sake, Clogs had floored Boots from behind with the wet cement, thereafter making off with the *haute couture*, while Boots lay on the ground shouting 'Stop thief!' or something of the sort.

In spite of the bang on the head, she was full of beans over tea, I remember, excitedly telling me about a new young man she had recently acquired. Quite forgetting my circle's first rule of etiquette, I asked her what he did for a living.

'He's an entrepreneur,' said Boots.

'That's nice,' I said.

'Yeah,' said Boots. 'He's a decorator. We've just split up.'

'That was quick,' I said.

'Relationships change fast in west London,' Boots said.

I didn't see her for a few weeks but, on Monday, she came to tea again. She was in frightful shape, as mad as a hatter, I thought, though a shade less obviously mad, perhaps, than Maxwell had always seemed. She drew the curtains, sat with a night-sighted air-rifle across her knees and spoke in a barely audible whisper, insisting that the room was bugged.

'Surely not,' I said. 'What's up?'

'They've got me,' she said. 'I've been broken by the system.'

A month ago, she said, her lorry had driven another into a ditch. Now she was to be prosecuted. It was a conspiracy, she said, to deprive her of her livelihood. They were all in it – the Prime Minister, Scotland Yard, the Law Society, the Masons, Clogs.

'It's well out of order,' she said. 'I can't work without my driving licence. Are they taking the piss or what?'

I suggested that she get about by bus, but she laughed at me scornfully.

'I don't use them facilities,' she said. 'Never have.'

She wasn't going down without a fight, however. She had written to the Ombudsman, to her MP and to old Lord Winterbottom, whoever he might be, explaining that she was being followed everywhere by the Special Branch and that her mail was being tampered with. In the circumstances, she told me, she had decided to defend herself in court since any barrister she might engage would be part of the conspiracy as well.

I went with her to court on Wednesday and stood at the back expecting to have a good laugh. Boots made a long speech, mentioning the Prime Minister, the Masons, Scotland Yard, old Lord Winterbottom, Clogs ('She's in it, m'lud') and the night-sighted air-rifle.

'It's a conspiracy, m'lud,' Boots concluded.

'I'm inclined to agree with you,' His Lordship said. 'Case dismissed.'

It shows what I know about insanity. Later, I rang Boots up to congratulate her.

'The odd thing is,' she said and then she slammed the receiver down.

That's got me thinking.

His Father's Gay

Unlike me, you may not have stood *in loco parentis* to Gay Kindersley's boy, Kim, so it will have been less of a surprise to you than it was to me that he's come up trumps at last – if making a film about a dolphin can properly be called coming up trumps.

The circumstances in which he passed himself off as mine for several weeks – bringing alcohol into my home, playing music that was six months out of date, leaving the bathroom as if a horse had been the last to use it and then making himself comfortable for the night in my literary room without first removing his clothes and make-up – do him little credit, I'm afraid, and I may even have touched on them before.

One evening, some years ago, I was, through a trivial misunderstanding, helping the police with their inquiries, when my first wife arrived with the bad news that my boy, Charlie, was at Eton and, further, that he was off the rails. He needed a father's influence, she said.

A sensible, house-holding woman dressed by Hermes and

with a voice that could have pierced a labrador's eardrums at a distance of five furlongs, she was seized by the police and bundled into the bedroom where she fell off the bed and on to the floor. ('Damn me, I'm on my arse here!')

I got off scot-free, I'm glad to say, whereas my visitors – a detective sergeant and three understrappers – drew an average of four years each: by no means an unusual result in the seventies before Sir Robert Mark's hasty PR job on the Metropolitan CID meant that wrongdoers found themselves on the wrong end of a prison sentence as often as the chaps who'd come to bang them up.

A few days later I went down to Eton, thereafter taking the wrong boy out to lunch; an easy enough mistake to make, I've always thought, particularly when you haven't seen yours since he was two years old. I arranged to meet him under the clock at Windsor station and assuming, wrongly, that there'd be some family resemblance I collared the first alert-looking lad I saw and marched him off to lunch.

I asked him the usual beefy questions – did he stack up in a rugger scrum and so forth? – whereupon he said that he didn't care to play rough games in the rain ('For pity's sake, Humphrey, you're standing on my hair!'), so I wrestled him to the floor.

'Please, sir, stop wrestling me to the floor,' he said.

'You don't have to call me sir,' I said. 'Call me Daddy.'

'You're not my father, sir,' he said.

I was scandalized, of course.

'How dare you suggest such a thing against your mother!' I said, and I wrestled him to the floor again.

Then he started to blub, or at least looked as if he might, so I asked him whether he'd like to leave Eton and live instead with me and his Aunty Cherry. He said he would, so we packed his tuck-box and returned to London without, I think, apprising the Dame of this change in his arrangements.

He was a nice enough lad and everything went pretty well until I received a telephone call one morning from the headmaster of Eton, Mr McCrum.

'We've lost your boy,' he said.

'Well done,' I said. 'Actually, I've got him here.'

At that moment my front-door bell rang. I asked the headmaster to hang on while I answered it. I opened the door to find

155

another boy standing outside who claimed that he was my son, Charlie.

'The devil you are,' I said. 'Charlie's asleep in my literary room.'

I went back to the telephone and told the headmaster that there was a bit of a mix-up. 'I seem to have two of them,' I said.

The headmaster suggested that I take them both back to Eton where he was able, in no time, to distinguish which was which. The second arrival was, indeed, my boy Charlie and the imposter turned out to be Gay Kindersley's boy, Kim. My boy Charlie was then expelled, I don't know why, whereas Kim, whose behaviour had been deplorable in my opinion, was taken back into the fold.

I then lost touch with Kim but such news as I got of him wasn't reassuring – not least that he'd become an actor. I agreed somewhat reluctantly, therefore, when he invited me to cruise up west this week to see a film about a dolphin which he'd written and directed.

If you've seen one dolphin turning somersaults, I always think, you've seen them all, but Kim's film turned out to be a master-piece. It looks lovely, if you like that sort of thing, and it makes the interesting point that the locals are as intelligent as the dolphin – which is certainly no stupider than others of its kind – and perhaps more intelligent, since they have had the wit to publicize its antics, turning what was once a dreary little fishing village into a concrete holiday complex with all the amenities.

When I got home, my boy Charlie rang.

'Can I speak to Daddy?' he said.

'He's moved,' I said.

You can't be too careful. He might be making a film about a dolphin, and one of them in the family is quite enough.

Dummett's Argument for God

I don't know about you, but as the *Oldie* gossip columnist I worked flat out over Christmas, keeping an ear to the ground but discovering only that Mrs Matthews, who is ninety-four and lives on the floor below, has cancelled her subscription to the *Independent* and plans henceforth to read the *Daily Telegraph*.

This is interesting, clearly, though whether it's interesting enough for a whole column in the *Oldie* only time will tell. Composing it was surprisingly difficult, I must admit – not because the material turned out to be unmanageable or meagre, but because the world (unusually at this time of the year) refused to go away.

As a general rule, Christmas comes as a welcome relief for thoughtful recluses such as myself, since all the people who press themselves on you at other times – blatantly ambitious friends, common publishers, sordid older women who, just because you're single and obviously well bred, are keen that you should take their daughters out – suddenly lose their reason and, as I've said before, I think, behave for a few days like *Spectator* diarists behave for the rest of the year: going to church, buying self-consciously witty presents for their friends, calling on their unpleasant relatives, visiting Scotland and spending time with their unsatisfactory children.

This year, unaccountably, I came under quite unexpected pressure to join in. I was invited to turkey lunches in so many homes, in fact, that rather than give offence I resorted to deceit – pretending that I'd broken my leg in three places and that I was thus obliged to stay indoors. This did the trick, but rather than be seen flying around Fulham in my usual energetic fashion, I affected a limp; further, and in order to build the part up from the outside ('start with the shoes,' Sir Ralph Richardson used to say – and is this why English actors, compared to their American counterparts, can't do it at all, I wonder?) I purchased a surgical stocking of the sort that French rugby players and old tarts collecting their pensions wear.

The surgical stocking, I soon discovered, cuts off the supply of blood to the leg and returning from the chemist's on Christmas Eve I was compelled to drag mine along behind me like a dead log for the grate. This was good ('Out of the old fool's way! Can't you see he's the *Oldie's* gossip columnist?') but within a stone's throw of my front door I sensed that I was being over-taken by old Mrs Matthews, ninety-four.

I didn't, obviously, want to get stuck with her since she isn't as lively as she used to be, so I accelerated slightly and fell on my face.

157

'Pull yourself together, dear,' she said. 'Have you been on the Ecstasy again? You know what happened last time.'

Two years ago, you may remember, I had a religious experience after taking Ecstasy in Ibiza with my literary agent, Alison. A materialistic interpretation of the world couldn't explain anything as perfect as her, I thought. Dummett's argument for God ('We *know* there is value. Value isn't part of the world. So a divine being must have put it there') seemed irrefutable and I needed urgently to describe my experience to any who'd listen, including Mrs Matthews. Mrs Matthews, in fact, had been most unsympathetic.

'Don't talk to me about religion,' she'd said. 'At my age, I can't be bothered with stuff like that.'

'As it happens,' I now said, 'I've broken my leg in three places.'

For some reason, Mrs Matthews seemed to find this very funny. 'Oh dear, oh, dear,' she said. 'That will stop you running around. I quite liked your column about Boots and your efforts to raise the wind. How is Boots, by the way?'

'In the pink, I'm glad to say. She's thinking of going into the car business, whatever that might be.'

'Really?' said Mrs Matthews. 'I used to be in the car business myself. I was planning to go back into it in 1992.'

'So you read the *Independent*?' I said.

'Not any more,' said Mrs Matthews. 'I've just cancelled my order. You've read today's editorial?'

'Not yet,' I confessed.

'Listen to this,' said Mrs Matthews, producing her copy and poking at the relevant passage with an indignant forefinger. '"Behaviour over Christmas is evidence for the truth of Christian belief."'

'What's wrong with that?'

'Everything,' said Mrs Matthews. 'It is to argue that Christianity is real because it produces real effects. The fact that people often do change after a religious experience does not itself show that the experience has been caused by a divine being. Such an argument equates the truth of a belief with its power to motivate. I've switched to the *Daily Telegraph*.'

We don't want to haemorrhage readers on Christmas Eve, so I generously invited her to a turkey dinner on Christmas Day.

'Certainly not,' she said. 'Christmas provides me with a rare opportunity to be on my own.'

It serves the ungracious old biddy right that I plan to ridicule her in the *Oldie*.

Mrs Matthews and the Tatler Types

Some months ago I made the mistake of having lunch with my old schoolfriend, Popper, whom I hadn't seen since 1956. After an hour or two of wooden chit-chat – 'Any news of Gibbons?' – I longed for something to be said that was revealing and meant, kind or unkind. I therefore broke the first rule of conversational etiquette in Popper's social class – which is to maintain at all times an undisturbing surface burble – and said:

'Are you happy?'

Popper's honest eyes bulged with discomfort. He wouldn't have been more surprised if I'd insulted his wife, his mother and his sister in one lewd outburst. He stared at me silently for a full minute and then said:

'Are you pulling my wire?'

I soon forgot this depressing incident, but remembered it again during the New Year's Eve party which my best friend Little Jo and I gave on Tuesday. I didn't mention the party here during its planning stage, partly because Little Jo asked me not to alert a lot of people to the fact that they hadn't been invited (Little Jo has recently taken her business from *Ritz* to *Tatler* and has, as a career move, sensibly dropped all her old friends), and partly to avoid gatecrashers.

My friends, of course, would never barge in ininvited, but when, thirty years ago, I'd been what Little Jo calls 'a *Tatler* sort of person', it had been the custom, I now remembered, of cadging young moneymen and their lardy, squealing girlfriends to walk into anyone's home for what they referred to as 'a free drink', thereafter firing champagne corks from Belgravia balconies on to the lower orders walking home from work.

159

I had no particular reason to suppose that the manners of the upper middle classes had improved in the intervening years, and the precaution, in any event, paid off. The only gatecrashers were Mrs Matthews, ninety-four, who, sadly, has let herself go a bit in the last few years and can't, as a consequence, be thought of as an asset at a party, and my temporary literary agent, Cat Ledger, who, whatever else you might say against her, certainly isn't 'a *Tatler* sort of person'.

I must say, I'd been caught on the hop when Little Jo first mentioned the idea two or three weeks ago. Apart from the Superbowl parties which Alison, my beloved, and I organize once a year (and they don't really count, amounting, as they do, to a group of seriously well-informed young people watching this most cerebral and gentlemanly of sports in silence and then being tipped into the night) I hadn't been involved at the sharp end of the party business since the sixties when we used to sit on the floor and hope for the best. Nor did there seem any good reason to break the habit now.

'Let's give a party together,' Little Jo had said.

'Why?'

'As you know,' Little Jo had said. 'I now work for *Tatler* and I'm keen to impress my new employers with my range of important contacts. Unfortunately, I don't have any. I thought I might borrow some of yours.'

That made sense, so I rang up Boots, Jillypoo and Andy from the Sixties, Black Simone, One-Eyed Charlie, and Baby Boo the Snake-Thin Inca and told them that they had to come to a New Year's Eve party since Little Jo wanted to impress some friends of hers on *Tatler*, further telling them that we might have a little sophisticated fun at their expense, shocking them slightly with our unconventional habits.

In the event, my lot sat on the floor and talked, while Little Jo's friends stood inanely with glasses in their hands, exchanging *badinage* – the only bridge between the two groups being Mrs Matthews and my temporary literary agent, Cat Ledger, who burst in together after Cat Ledger, who can sniff an opportunity to network at a distance of three postal districts, had rung on Mrs Matthews's doorbell by mistake.

While Cat Ledger and Mrs Matthews mingled, I sat on the floor with my group, shortly having a large idea. Gossip, I realized, was a social prophylactic in the class to which these *Tatler* types belonged, a device to avoid the expression of real feelings, equally a security blanket, bonding them – as at school – under a warm, embracing glow of nicknames and thoughtless banter. My friends, on the other hand, being less driven by the need to conform, were not afraid to *talk*.

'Gossiping, are they?' I said to Mrs Matthews who, exhausted, I imagined, by the incessant surface burble to which she'd been subjected, had now joined me and my friends in our corner of the room.

'Not at all,' she said. 'In fact they find it a little slow here and now plan to move to a barricaded basement in Notting Hill where they intend to chase the dragon. Come along everyone.'

They all walked out – Mrs Matthews and the *Tatler* types and my sheep-like friends – and since it's a lonely business being left on your own at 11.30 on New Year's Eve, I rang up my old schoolfriend Popper.

'Any news of Gibbons?' I said.

Edited by a Floor-walker at Conran Octopus

The good news is that Mrs Matthews, ninety-four, who, as you may remember, gave up the *Independent* on Christmas Eve (she had spotted a philosophical disaster in that day's editorial), is back in the fold after a brief flirtation with the *Daily Telegraph*.

I discovered this in the course of a rather ill-conceived dinner party at my place on Saturday night in honour of Wole Soyinka who, as you'll know, won the Nobel Prize for Literature in 1986. It had been my good fortune to meet Professor Soyinka in 1974 when he was Overseas Fellow at Churchill College, Cambridge, where he wrote his widely acclaimed *Death and the King's Horsemen*.

I say the party was ill-conceived since my guests, rather than listen to Mrs Matthews's reasons for giving up the *Telegraph*, would have preferred, obviously, to watch the Denver Broncos stuffing the Houston Oilers on television (and while we must take our hats off to John Elway, I suppose, for converting no fewer than two fourth downs in that final extraordinary drive, he should thank his lucky stars, I think, that he wasn't intercepted with his absurd ballooning pass on third down and ten while still miles out of field-goal range).

'The *Telegraph*'s nervy desire to be correct,' Mrs Matthews explained, 'turned out to be a little too overwhelming for my taste.'

'What do you mean?' I said.

'I refer,' said Mrs Matthews, 'to the *Telegraph*'s priggish, assumed interest – where none obviously exists – in the activities of the more worthless members of the Royal Family; equally, to its sanctimonious insistence that "duffel-coated activists" who dispute the right of fat men in fancy dress to disembowel small animals in open fields – thereafter getting pie-eyed and, on the way home, driving their Range Rovers into bollards – are guilty of something called "the New Puritanism", a condition recently diagnosed in the *Telegraph* by Dr John Casey as afflicting anyone who doesn't share that paper's rather unpleasant dispositions.'

'I wonder what's on television,' Professor Soyinka said. 'American football, do you suppose?'

'Dr Casey,' continued Mrs Matthews, 'shouldn't, as a respectable academic, accept commissions from middle-market enterprises to spell out what is and isn't politically correct. Wake yourself up, dear.'

This last remark was addressed to me, I think, and I had indeed been guilty of drifting off – not only because I would rather have been watching the American football, but also because I was in the grip of a large problem: should I tell Professor Soyinka that he was not, as he had always supposed, edited at Methuen by our mutual friend Geoffrey Strachan, but by a floorwalker at Conran Octopus (incorporating Methuen), an enterprise which, if I'm not mistaken, sells triangular lampshades and bathroom tiles?

I have referred before, I think, to the discomforts of being edited, which are indeed many and grievous. You write something to the best of your abilities – for television, say, or for publication as a book – and hand it in, imagining, for some reason, that that's the last you will hear of it. Not a bit of it. A whole series of people in offices, of whom you'd not previously heard – producers, rights personnel, accountants, women – express an interest in what you've written, boast even of some expertise in assessing it, when half an hour watching television or a quick trip to a book shop will tell you in all likelihood that their opinion will be of less interest than the cleaning lady's.

My friend Gerry Sadowitz, the brilliant young comedian, has an effective way of dealing with the problem. Confronted by a woman who, until recently, has been someone's secretary, he asks her what her opinion of Ben Elton is, and, unless she immediately turns pea-green and holds on to the furniture, he thanks her for her time, gathers up his manuscript and takes it down the corridor. I, on the other hand, listen to her courteously, and then go home and get into bed.

Be that as it may, none of this arises if you're being edited by Geoffrey Strachan whose opinion on what you've written is probably as interesting as your own, if not more so. On Saturday, however, I was obliged to call on him at Methuen where I was fielded by a young man who was wearing a security guard's tunic above floorwalker's trousers. I gave him my name, whereupon he told me that he had recently edited my book, *Root Into Europe*, which is to be published by Methuen in May.

'Generally,' he said, 'I work as a floorwalker at Conran Octopus, but at weekends I double as a security guard for Methuen. When Geoffrey's busy, he passes work on to me.'

The question was, should I tell Professor Soyinka? In the end, I decided not to.

'This business of being edited . . .' I said.

'No problem,' Professor Soyinka said. 'My stuff's cut by a floorwalker at Conran Octopus, whose judgement, after all, is likely to be as sound as any other unqualified person's. Couldn't we watch the American football now?'

Ingrams Plans to Humiliate Our Old Folk

We've lost Mrs Matthews again, I'm afraid, and this time it's down to Lynn Barber, of all people. Disappointed by what she took to be a mistake by Miss Barber in last week's *Independent on Sunday*, Mrs Matthews, ninety-four, traded it in for a copy of the *Sunday Telegraph* – and it's as well she did, otherwise I might have devoted my first column in the *Oldie* to an extremely laborious joke, already used by the *Telegraph*.

Like you, I imagine, I have been brooding for a few weeks on what on earth the point of the *Oldie* could be, and, until Mrs Matthews told me otherwise, I thought I'd cracked it.

In the run-up to its first edition, the assumption has been, I think, that Richard Ingrams, the *Oldie*'s editor, had detected a gap in the market, but this, I decided, could not be so. While the *Telegraph, Spectator* and *Private Eye* continue to flourish, indignant old men could not reasonably complain that their tastes were inadequately catered for.

I've therefore decided that Ingrams's plan must be to hold these unhappy seniors up to ridicule – quite a cruel idea on the face of it, but one with humorous, if limited, possibilities. In spite of the fact that Ingrams was once the target of the only joke Jeremy Isaacs is thought to have made ('If Leibniz was the last man to know everything, Ingrams must be counted the first man to know nothing'), he is an accomplished editor and had been influenced on this occasion, I decided, by a piece of advice from Groucho Marx.

Marx, you may remember, said that an amateur, to raise a laugh, would dress a young man up as an old woman and send him hurtling down a steep hill in a wheelchair, but for a professional it would have to be a real woman.

That was it, then, Ingrams planned to humiliate our old folk, and I shortly came up with an idea that would fit excellently, I thought, into this editorial design. I'd ring up a lot of broken old men – embittered journalists, once-fashionable playwrights, etc – and ask them what they thought of the young these days. Not only would I be ridiculing myself for having had such an impertinently tired idea, but, as important, my interviewees could be relied on to make idiots of themselves by saying that the young knew nothing, couldn't write English and played music too loudly in public places.

I was pretty pleased with myself and I continued so until Wednesday this week when, on the way to discuss my idea with Ingrams over lunch, I tried it out on Mrs Matthews whom I met on the stairs.

'Too late,' she said. 'You've been scooped by the *Sunday Telegraph*. This week they ran the very same joke, even carrying it over into the books pages where Dirk Bogarde reminded us – while reviewing *Stephen Hawking: A Life in Science* – that Bernard Levin had once said that he had been unable to get beyond page twenty-nine of *A Brief History of Time*. Mr Levin's remark had surprised me. While nothing he had written for thirty years would have led one to think he was intelligent enough to understand Professor Hawking's ideas, one would have supposed he was intelligent enough not to boast about it.'

'I thought you'd given up the *Telegraph* and were back with the *Independent*,' I said.

'And so I was,' said Mrs Matthews, 'until this week when I spotted a mistake by the usually excellent Lynn Barber. Discussing breaking the law and a sense of shame, Miss Barber seemed to suggest that breaking the law was wrong in itself – a notion which, if true, would entail our being punished twice: once, say, for stealing an old lady's purse; then again for breaking the law. The fact is that reasonable people would rightly feel some shame for breaking certain laws – driving when drunk comes to mind – but none at all for breaking others, smoking cannabis, for instance.'

'Never mind all that,' I said. 'What, then, should I write for the *Oldie*?'

'A straightforward gossip column,' said Mrs Matthews. 'Didn't Sir Victor Pritchett say recently that the only thing he'd learnt for certain in the course of a long life was that everyone eventually wants to be respectable? If this is so, it certainly follows that where this desire is keenest – among the people who compose *Private Eye*, for instance – a prurient interest in gossip will flourish. Only a repressed public schoolboy is excited to discover that someone has taken his secretary to Brighton.'

Mrs Matthews was undoubtedly right, I thought, and over lunch with Ingrams I sought to reassure him that I was an incomparable source of locker-room tittle-tattle. He let me blunder on for a bit and then he said that I'd got the wrong end of the stick entirely.

'My plan,' he said, 'is that we old folk should hold ourselves up to ridicule, the only dignified role available to us still – and no one does this better, albeit unwittingly, than you. Write your usual stuff, boasting about taking drugs with the young and so forth. However, if you really want people to believe you're on terms with Gerry Sadowitz, the brilliant young comedian, you should discover, perhaps, how to spell his name.'

I blame Mrs Matthews.

Abby from the Eighties and a Real Man

When Robert Kee first came down from university he lodged for a while in Chelsea with Augustus John who was well over eighty at the time. Mr Kee, who wasn't noticeably unattractive even as a young man, has told us somewhere that he didn't much care for this arrangement since he was irritated beyond measure by the procession of beautiful young women who queued up outside Mr John's bedroom door.

On one occasion, after Mr John had retired with no fewer than four young women, Mr Kee was kept awake all night by moose-like jungle howls, the furious demands of women intent on pleasure, and the sound of breaking furniture coming from the room next door.

In the morning Mr John came down to breakfast in terrible shape. He was wearing his trousers back to front, his shirt was torn and he had blood on his beard. 'Sorry about that, Kee,' he said. 'Bit of a roughhouse last night.'

I was reminded of this on Saturday when I had a bit of a roughhouse at my place. I wouldn't normally embarrass myself and you by describing the incident, but I have been brooding on

166

my discovery – mentioned here last week – that Richard Ingrams wanted to employ me on the *Oldie* simply to make a fool of myself.

This has always been something I've been at pains not to do – perhaps mistakenly, I now realize. It's the case, after all, that our preferred reading – in journalism, at least – is stuff that treads a fine line between making us squint with indignation and embarrassing us so much that we want to get into bed and hide.

As our second Sunday paper, you and I would, obviously rather take the *Telegraph* – which has us in a towering rage even before we've opened it – than the *Observer*, say, with whose opinions we by and large agree. Equally, the best, or at least, the most celebrated columnists – like the fat exhibitionists who appear on fraudulently improvised television shows and comical news quizzes – are happy to please us by making asses of themselves, to risk our enduring ridicule (and thanks) by being altogether too revealing about themselves.

Accordingly, I now tend to go too far myself, to embarrass myself and you by being altogether too revealing about my old friend Andy from the Sixties and my new friend Abby from the Eighties. Andy from the Sixties is a real man, dominant and busy, a former Mr Fulham Broadway who can still squat-lift a grand piano. More importantly, he left school at fourteen and was a millionaire by the time he was nineteen.

He thinks I'm a half-wit but Abby from the Eighties, who is a fine example of a real woman – pouting and treacherous, recklessly abject and devouring, but, because of the shortage of real men these days, obliged all too often to pay over the odds for what she wants – has taken to dropping in at my place in the evening on her way to work because, as she says, she likes my mind.

'I'm bored,' she said on Saturday evening. 'I half fancy a hammering. Don't you know any real men? I'll pay.'

'There's Andy from the Sixties,' I said. 'Stomach like an ironing board. Twinkling legs.'

'He'll do,' she said. 'I'll be back after work.'

I booked Andy from the Sixties and then I remembered that I wasn't altogether without experience in this department myself. Some years ago, Dawn Upstairs told me about a client of hers – a well-to-do Sikh – who from time to time liked to arrange something for his mistress. She had run through all of Dawn Upstairs's young men – Steve the Stud, Andy from the Sixties, etc – and now she wanted something different.

'Do you happen to know an English gentleman?' Dawn Upstairs had said.

'I'm an English gentleman,' I said.

'You haven't got estates and that,' she said.

'I'll do it as the Duke of Marlborough,' I said.

And so I had – further, and unlike Steve the Stud and Andy from the Sixties, being asked for repeatedly again, not that I ever obliged.

When Andy from the Sixties came over, I reminded him of this. 'Don't be too confident,' I said. 'Remember the Sikh's mistress? She never asked for *you* again.'

'I put that down to class,' said Andy from the Sixties.

He was forgetting that Abby from the Eighties liked my mind.

They're odd creatures, women, after all. In Abby from the Eighties's shoes, which would you have preferred? A fit young man with a washboard stomach and twinkling toes, or a sordid old-timer in a surgical stocking?

The fit young man, of course, and Abby from the Eighties was no exception. While I was in the kitchen for a minute, what sounded like a pub fight broke out in my drawing-room and when I returned Andy from the Sixties was staggering around on spaghetti legs, counting his money, and Abby from the Eighties was on her way out of my front door with a silly expression on her face.

'So you pulled it,' I said.

'Of course,' said Andy from the Sixties. 'I used my mind. I did it as the Duke of Marlborough. I'm not stupid.'

Shopping with my Gazza Knee

Until last Saturday the most gruelling shopping experience I'd had was buying a handbag in Florence for my literary agent, Alison. Since every other shop in the place sells the things, I'd imagined that our business would be completed in five minutes flat, but not a bit of it. We trailed around for three hours while Alison rejected every bag on offer and then she fainted with excitement over one in a window that was exactly like the others.

When it comes to buying a suit my friend Craig Brown seems to have as clear an idea of what he wants. If you or I wanted a suit we'd hop into the nearest suit shop and say, 'Hullo, I'm after a suit,' departing a minute later with something appropriate.

On Saturday Craig Brown walked me up and down the King's Road with my gammy leg and now, as a consequence, it appears that I may be unable to organize the Academy Club's defence (judged, hitherto, to be a little naïve) in their important, soccer fixture against the Groucho Club.

It had been touch and go whether I could take part in this match in any case. No day is so good that giving the Groucho Club a stuffing doesn't make it better but, when Mr Waugh first invited me to play, I hesitated slightly, pointing out that soccer was very much my third skill (some way behind American football and rugger) and, more importantly, that I was carrying an injury – had been, indeed, for the past thirty years.

'You'll remember Cambridge's rugger team of '58?' I said.

'No,' said Mr Waugh.

I was surprised, but I pressed on. 'Fifteen full internationals,' I said. 'Andy Mulligan, Phil Horrocks-Taylor, David Marques, Geoffrey Windsor-Lewis and the incomparable Arthur Smith on the right-wing. "Give it to Arthur!" we used to shout.

'Be that as it may, I was challenging Andy Mulligan all season for the scrum-half's shirt, and then in a practice game I did my right knee when falling on the ball under half a hundredweight of opposition forwards. I never played rugger again, but what a team!'

'What happened?' asked Mr Waugh.

'What happened when?'

'In the varsity match?'

'Cambridge got stuffed,' I said. 'Oxford, as was their custom in those days filled the team with fourteen South Africans and a little Welshman – Olwyn Brace, was it?'

In the event, Mr Waugh refused to let me off the hook. Gary Lineker had agreed to turn out for the Groucho Club, he said, and the feeling among the Academy Club's coaching staff was that only I, playing is my old position of sweeper – albeit on one leg – could hope to contain him.

'You may have slowed down a bit,' he said, 'but as Bob Paisley used to say about Kenny Dalglish – a fat old carthorse like yourself – "the first yard's in the mind" You only need one leg when turning on a sixpence in front of goal and putting the ball in the back of the net.'

'I won't be in front of goal,' I said.

'Nor you will,' said Mr Waugh. 'I'm relying on you none the less.'

I thought I should do something about my knee so, being a naval man (when shipping it green at ninety feet one doesn't have time for doctors anaesthetics and so forth), I removed the cartilege with an oyster fork and was confident that I'd be match fit for the big game. I hadn't calculated that Craig Brown might ask me out to lunch.

'I've got a column to write,' I said to him. 'What are the chances of your saying something amusing or indiscreet?'

'That's not very gracious,' he said.

'Never mind gracious,' I said. 'To me you're just 22 stone of possible copy in a funny hat.'

'I'll do my best,' he said.

His best, alas, wasn't good enough and after an hour or two I had to tell him that there was nothing in my writer's notebook – kept open, just in case, beside the knives and forks – that I could use.

'I'll take you shopping,' he said. 'I want to buy a suit from Stephen King.'

That seemed odd, but I was reassured to discover that Mr King traded just around the corner.

'Have you got any suits?' asked Craig Brown.

'No,' said a man who I supposed was Stephen King, so we walked out.

That's what happens, I thought, if you try to buy a suit from a man who normally writes horror books, and I imagined that that would be the end of the matter.

Brown, alas, had other ideas and for the next hour he ran me up and down the King's Road, quite ignoring all the suit shops, but occasionally diving into little basement establishments in which strange young men insisted, like Mr King, that they didn't have any suits. By the time we reached Sloane Square, I was limping badly.

'I'll be off now,' said Brown.

'You're going to leave me here?' I said. 'I can't walk.'

'Maybe not,' he said. 'But I've given you a column.'

That was true, but who now will contain Gary Lineker?

Yo's Out, Wally's In

I've had a startingly commercial idea – more accurately, Mrs Matthews has and my only problem now is how to separate her from the substantial profits likely to accrue. She has also received a black eye, which I spotted on Monday when I met her on the stairs. She must have had a fall, I thought, but to have made sympathetic inquiries along these lines would have been unpardonably insulting.

'Been in another fight?' I said, congratulating myself even as I spoke on my deft, unpatronising touch with proud old tarts of ninety-four.

'Yes,' she said. Then she explained that she'd had an altercation at the Tuck Box – a senior citizens' tearoom, I assumed.

'Did someone pinch the last cream bun?' I said.

'Wake yourself up, dear,' she said. 'The Tuck Box is the barricaded basement in Notting Hill which I first visited with your best friend, Little Jo, on New Year's Eve. Rastafarians with guns. Fat little *Tatler* girls quacking with excitement. Pipes, Bunsen burners. A disinherited aristocrat or two licking the carpet. Will Self doing research.'

'How interesting,' I said.

'Not in the least,' she said.

'Such places, in fact, are exactly as one's maiden aunt – or your sister Bobo – would imagine them to be. One learns nothing, I'm afraid. An intoxicated *Tatler* girl talks, all too predictably, like an intoxicated *Tatler* girl. A peak-time television playwright would be hard pressed not to catch it accurately. Be that as it may, I was in a heated musical dispute with Evans the Rock, when half a hundredweight of local old Bill came headfirst through the front door.

'Not so well barricaded after all,' I said.

'Precisely,' said Mrs Matthews. 'Worse, I happened to be holding a bag of the best Peruvian Pink. "Hullo hullo, what's this, then?" one of the old Bill said, emptying the contents into the palm of his hand. "What's what?" I said. Then I affected a shattering sneeze which blew the stuff all over the room – a trick I learnt sixty years ago. Old Bill doesn't like it, of course. You expect a bit of a slapping – hence the black eye.'

'Never mind all that,' I said. 'What caused your musical dispute with Evans the Rock?'

'I was maintaining that what we in the music business call "wally records" are an insult to today's youth.'

'What's a "wally record".'

'Oh dear, oh dear,' said Mrs Matthews. 'Some ageing opportunist – Andrew Lloyd Webber, say – takes a comic old song and reissues it as dance music. That's 120 b.p.m. "The Itsy Bitsy Teeny Weeny Yellow Polka Dot Bikini" was it? Such stuff is very big in Benidorm and Brighton. We should produce one, in fact, to be released at the same time as *Root Into Europe*. George Cole singing "The Lambeth Walk" in Ibiza. It could be big. I'll alert my people at London Records. Currently they're doing nothing but Yo music. That's lounging young men wearing their baseball hats back to front. A wally record will make an agreeable change.'

I ran back to my place and got straight on the telephone to London Records. I'd have to move like lightning here. Pulling a fast one on Mrs Matthews would be easy, but it was important that my associates on *Root Into Europe* – Mark Chapman, the director, and the producer, Justin Judd – didn't get wind of my intentions. It was of the essence that I cut them out financially, on top of which a blind man on a dark night wouldn't mistake either of them for music-business types – least of all Justin Judd who now spends most of his time on his estate in Norfolk and, as a consequence, wears plus-fours in Percy Street and carries a cocked 12-bore as he goes about his other business.

'Hullo, hullo. London Records?' I said. 'Here's one. What we in the music business call a wally record. George Cole singing "The Lambeth Walk"! Done as dance music. That's 120 b.p.m. Kindly alert your A & R department.'

172

'Can you tell me who you're with?'

'Mrs Matthews.'

That did the trick. After a whispered backstage conference, the telephonist said that Tracey Bennett would meet me at Kensington Place restaurant on Wednesday week. I managed to hide my surprise that London Records was being run by a slip of a girl.

'She'll do,' I said.

'And bring a Dat,' the telephonist said.

What the hell was that? Luckily, I bumped into Mrs Matthews again that evening.

'Have you been on to London Records?' she said.

'Certainly not,' I said. 'What's a Dat, by the way?'

'A digital audio tape,' she said. 'The days are gone when you could get on the telephone to a record company and whistle a tune down the line. These days, they like the finished product. I'd better introduce you to Evans the Rock. He's got a studio.'

This is all very exciting. As long as Judd and Chapman don't discover what I'm up to I'll be off-shore by Easter in a striped shirt and canary yellow yomping boots.

Off-shore with Dawn Upstairs

Last week I said here (not too boastfully, I hope) that as a consequence of my entry into the music business – more accurately, my re-entry, since I once represented P.J. Proby, Peter, Paul and Mary and goodness knows who else – I'd be offshore by Easter, eating chicken on Sundays and wearing canary yellow yomping boots.

In the event, I'm offshore already. Following my discovery that Dawn Upstairs is being chased by Mrs Lamb of the Inland Revenue for tax on a million pounds, I've moved like lightning, opening bank accounts in the Isle of Man, Guernsey, Jersey and Andorra.

It's an illwind, indeed. Dawn Upstairs's misfortune has been a stroke of luck for me, alerting me to difficulties ahead and allowing me to hide from Mrs Lamb the torrent of money that will roll in after my meeting with Tracey Bennett of London Records. (In fact, Dawn Upstairs told Mrs Lamb to get stuffed, but this option, though appealing, will not be available to me, I think, since my name will shortly be synonymous in the music business with fiscal probity and sound management.)

Nor, apart from these arrangements, have I been sitting here twiddling my thumbs. Tracey Bennett, who, you may remember, fell hook, line and sinker for my suggestion that we should record George Cole singing 'The Lambeth Walk', asked me to pitch up with the finished product – a request which, since I don't have a studio at the moment, entailed a quick search in the King's Road for a temporary partner whom I'd phase out tactfully once the profits started to accrue.

I ran into the Dome brasserie and cast my eye over the assembled young men who, since they'd been up since tea time, were now slumped with exhaustion over their croissants and coffee. One seemed more alert than the others so I asked him whether he had access to a recording studio.

'Of course,' he said.

So far, so good. I explained the dodge and then – in order that he shouldn't suppose I was in town for the day on an old folks' bus pass – I gave him some background on myself, pointing out that I'd once represented Peter, Paul and Mary.

'Were they the blind ones?' he said.

Young people. If it happened the day before yesterday, they haven't heard of it.

'At the moment,' I said, 'I'm treating with Tracey Bennett of London Records. Have you heard of her? She wants the finished product. The days are gone, alas, when you could get on the phone to a record company, whistle a tune down the line and be on *Top of the Pops* the next day.'

'You're telling me,' said my new, temporary partner, who's called Simon Holiday, though that's neither here nor there. 'Do you own the rights?'

I'd got one here. I might have done better, I thought, not to have elbowed Mrs Matthews who wanted to introduce me to her recording expert, Evans the Rock.

'And what about George Cole?' said young Holiday.

'We're in luck,' I said. 'He's in Australia, so he won't know what we're up to.'

174

'In that case we won't be able to supply the finished product.'

'Damn me, nor we will.' I must have looked quite cast down because young Holiday sought now to cheer me up.

'Never mind,' he said. 'I'll have a word with Corda Marshall of RCA. Meanwhile, you'd better get a music business haircut.'

I made an appointment with Miss Vicky of *Rodney et cie* – who, coincidentally, also does Dawn Upstairs's head – and it's as well I did, since otherwise I might still be sitting here like the last pin in a bowling alley, waiting for Mrs Lamb to pot me.

'Dawn Upstairs been in?' I said.

'I saw her yesterday,' said Miss Vicky. 'She's being chased by Mrs Lamb for tax on a million pounds. "You're doing well, Dawn Upstairs," I said. "It's the parking problem, Miss Vicky," she said. "A businessman fancies seeing a London girl and then he thinks, what about the car? I'll see Dawn Upstairs in Bassingstoke." She's told Mrs Lamb to get stuffed, but she's working flat out none the less. She had her mobile phone with her and made six appointments for that evening.

"It's £100," she said, "£150 for domination". My other ladies were well intrigued. "You're working too hard, Dawn Upstairs," I said. "They're all on my way home, Miss Vicky," she said. "They're a lot of people on their way home, Dawn Upstairs," I said, "but they're not all stopping off to give domination at £150 a time. You should go off-shore. You don't want Mrs Lamb coming after you."'

Miss Vicky was right about that and no mistake, so I ran back to my place and made the necessary arrangements. Then I telephoned my temporary partner, Simon Holiday.

'I don't want you burning the candle at both ends,' I said. 'Early to bed, no groupies, no drugs and up at 8.a.m.'

'Absolutely,' he said.

'You're not carrying, by any chance?'

'Certainly not.'

This won't be much fun. I might have done better to stick with Mrs Matthews and Evans the Rock.

The Groucho Club Gets Stuffed

Soccer they say, is a game of two halves, and never was the truth of this old saw better demonstrated than in the Derby on Sunday between the Academy Club and the Groucho Club. We stuffed them in the first half, then we changed ends and stuffed them again in the second half. All credit to the lads, especially me.

You'll gather that in spite of my Gazza knee, I eventually gave in to Mr Waugh's urgent request that I should organize the Academy's defence from my old position of centre-back. And I'm sorry I did because my leg has subsequently stiffened like a board, obliging me to postpone my important music–business rendezvous this week with Tracey Bennett of London Records.

Soccer is a girls' game, of course, and I had assumed – rightly, as it turned out – that a chap who'd once been on the winning side against Southampton (albeit when they were still in the Second Division) only had to turn up, keep an eye on things at the back, ghost through the opposition defence a couple of times, turn on a sixpence in front of goal and slot the ball in the back of the net with his educated left foot; thereafter modestly accepting the applause of the two mad women and a dog who'd bruised along to watch.

Which isn't to say that I didn't seek advice of a professional nature before finally accepting Mr Waugh's invitation. In fact, I rang up my old friend Colin Todd, now assistant manager of Millwall, but once the most cultured central defender ever to pull on the No 6 shirt for England.

Built like a brick shit-house, but as quick as a whippet, Toddy found the game so ridiculously easy that, like extravagantly gifted exponents of other sports (David Gower, Jimmy White and Deion Sanders, the Atlanta Falcons' corner-back, come to mind) he'd sometimes lose concentration and commit a majestic blunder in front of goal – the upshot being that a succession of bone-headed managers often replaced him in the England line-up with a persevering donkey such as Norman Hunter or Liverpool's Phil Thompson.

I rang Toddy up and told him I might turn out in the big match on Sunday. 'I'm surprised,' he said. 'I wouldn't be seen dead in the Groucho Club. A collection of squalid old raconteurs

176

and ambitious women with bad legs. Anyone who's had the misfortune to spend half an hour there will have a good idea of what their football team is like: flash, incompetent and common.'

'I'm not playing for the Groucho, Toddy,' I said. 'I'm playing for the Academy. We're all writers, as the name suggests, except, of course, for Terence Blacker. No, no – that's a joke. In fact, Blacker's exciting new novel – *Fame Hotel* – is my tip for this year's Booker Prize.'

'Mine too,' said Toddy. 'Can they play at all?'

'May I resort to an analogy?'

'By all means.'

'You'll remember Keith Miller, Australia's legendary all-rounder? At the end of the fifth day of the Lords Test of '53, Australia were 176 for 6, with Miller O not out. They needed 72 to win and Laker and Lock were bowling on a sticky wicket. No one gave Australia a chance. Miller, a true Corinthian, went out dancing that night, and came to the wicket the next morning in his dinner jacket and disco pumps, carrying a bat that he'd borrowed from a schoolboy. He was bowled first ball. That's the Academy Club for you. Nothing to wear and no bloody good. Plus, I've got a bad knee.'

'Follow the example of Franz Beckenbauer,' Toddy said. 'At the end of his career the Emperor Franz invented the position of sweeper behind the goalkeeper. In his last twenty internationals he never came within fifty yards of an opposition player. You'll be all right.'

And so I was. The Groucho's team – agents, publishers, vulgar young men who produced corporate videos, I imagine – beat themselves, running on to the field in new boots and with their mobile phones switched on. We put two past them in the first half and two more in the second, but they could have scored six themselves.

It's just as well I was there to marshal our defence. Talk about naive. Terence Blacker spent the afternoon snapping at the heels of their left-back – and he was our goalkeeper. Luckily, I kept my head. Whenever their big lad in the No 9 shirt got within range I managed, from my position behind the goalkeeper (not that we had one) to bring him up short by saying: 'I was surprised not to see you at Ed Victor's party last night,' or, 'Three of your best clients were seen dining at the Groucho Club on Friday with my own agents, Dunlop and Bollock-Brain.'

The big lad would turn as white as herring-roe and put himself urgently through to his personal secretary on his mobile phone.

It was a doddle but on Monday morning, I couldn't walk, so I was obliged to cancel my meeting with Tracey Bennett. My luck held, however. According to her secretary, she'd played for Globe on Saturday and was now carrying an injury herself. I said soccer was a girls' game.

Rent Boys, Drug Fiends and Confessions in the Sun

There is less money in the music business, it seems, than you and I might have supposed. Indeed, it is not unusual for turns with a Top 10 hit to be reduced to shoplifting in order to make ends meet. In the space of six months they buy a house and a car, are interviewed by Melvyn Bragg and then they go bankrupt.

I discovered this in the course of my lunch on Wednesday with Tracey Bennett of London Records, and I only hope that George Cole doesn't discover it, too.

Mr Cole, you may remember, is to record 'The Lambeth Walk' to coincide with the screening in June of *Root Into Europe* (not that he knows this yet himself) and while it would be regrettable if, thanks to me, he were to be arrested for running through Selfridges disguied as an enormous poacher's pocket – thereafter losing everything, including his delightful house – it would be even more regrettable if someone were to warn him of the difficulties ahead, causing him to cancel such arrangements as I might have made on his behalf.

I have also discovered that it is not unknown for a pop *artiste's* connections – managers, agents, bodyguards, etc – to get caught up in the financial catastrophe that is the inevitable consequence of a No 1 hit, and, in an abrupt *volte face*, I have accordingly reversed my policy of keeping in the dark anyone else who might suppose he has an interest in the matter, not least the producer of *Root Into Europe*, Justin Judd. To be on the safe side, I now go everywhere as Judd and sign his name on any piece of paper that is put in front of me: letters, restaurant bills, laundry lists and so forth.

I run ahead of myself, however. I knew none of this when I pitched up on Wednesday at Kensington Place restaurant for my rendezvous with Tracey Bennett. I was still in my fool's paradise, in fact; was delighted with myself for having prudently made offshore arrangements for the substantial windfall that was about to come my way; was confident, indeed, that before we'd finished the fish soup we'd have this slip of a girl over a barrel.

Don't misunderstand me. While it is true that in my day the music business was run by men, and by old men at that (courteous, if slightly common chaps with heads like racing tadpoles; ex-saxophonists in strict-tempo dance ensembles, who now had pictures on their desks of the wife and kids at home in Hertfordshire, were members, indeed, of the Lord's Taverners and Water Rats), I bow to no one in my belief that a woman should work – until, that is, she meets that special man and is able at last to fulfil her destiny by making him her whole existence.

Nor, these days, is there any shortage of jobs in which a woman of pleasing looks can exercise her feminine skills: PA to my friend Lord Weidenfeld, perhaps; a little not-too-serious desk editing for one of our more reputable houses ('OK by you Geoffrey if I have Friday orf? Benjie's taking me to Yorkshire'); Arts Editor of *Tatler*. That a young woman, however, should find herself playing away against an experienced old-time entrepreneur such as myself seemed to me a mismatch that could only end in tears. I was brooding along these lines when a burly fellow of cheerful aspect approached.

'William, is it?' he said.

'Yes,' I said, whereupon he sat down and ordered himself a gin and tonic. That's odd, I thought, but then I realized he must be Tracey's chauffeur.

'Will Tracey be long?' I said.

'I'm Tracey,' she said.

I take my hat off to her. Here was a woman of – let's face it – a most unfortunate appearance, yet she didn't care. Hair done in a 2-Para back and sides; no make-up and a music business suit that would have accommodated Jonathan Ross as well as herself.

She came straight to the point. 'I like the concept,' she said. 'George Cole singing "The Lambeth Walk" could go to No 1. But there's no money in singles. I've had bands with a No 1 who are still shoplifting to fill the fridge. They acquire a fistful of credit cards, buy a house and a car, and then get a royalty statement for £13.77. They, and their inexperienced advisers, are bankrupt within the year. Even Robert Stigwood went bust twice before he found the Bee Gees.'

'Charmaine and Diane,' I said. 'They were two of them.'

'The bachelors,' she said.

'You're telling me,' I said.

Suddenly I saw it all. The hideous timbered house in Windsor. The toothless veteran in Liverpool claiming to be my father and asking for a timbered house as well. Rent boys. Two-way mirrors. Drug fiends. The hair transplant and the confession in the sun: 'How cocaine ruined my life. And how I was saved by my love for a Russian seaman.' Thereafter, disgrace and bankruptcy.

'I'll be off now,' I said.

'If you want to supply me with the finished product, William . . .'

'Justin,' I said.

'What happened to William?' Tracey said.

'He couldn't make it,' I said. 'Send the bill to Justin Judd, c/o Aspect Productions, Percy Street. See you in the charts, my dear.'

I'm not stupid.

The Old Ones are Still the Best

I hesitate to say this about such a talented and amiable young man as Jeremy Lovering, but the compliments lavished upon him since he replaced me as the writer of *Root Into Europe* may have gone to his head, I think. Whereas I have accepted the situation with good grace, recognizing that such withering humiliations are in the natural order of things, he can't find a hat to fit him.

On Wednesday he pointed out that once *Root Into Europe* had been screened, my entire *oeuvre* would be associated inevitably with him and that I was no longer responsible, therefore, merely for my reputation but for his as well. Then he rebuked me for saying in last week's column that I could see no reason why a young woman of pleasing appearance shouldn't work for a while – until, that is, she found that special man with whom she could fulfil her feminine destiny by making him her whole existence.

'That was a joke,' I said.

'And of the sort that is no longer acceptable,' he said.

I blame the sixties. The breakdown of the family. Left wing food. Women taking responsibility for their own bodies. *Hair*, was it? The Princess Royal jack-naked on the stage. Woodstock and the Isle of Wight. Bob Dylan, the poet of the open road. A blowin' in the wind. Don't tell me. I'm in the music business.

'You've caused me considerable embarrassment,' Lovering continued. 'I move in mixed company and have now been banned from my local *cineastes*' workshop which was to have been addressed next week by Ben Elton.'

Lovering paused, politely suggesting, by means of a small hand signal, that I might for a moment have the floor.

'Do you wish to make a disparaging remark about Ben Elton?' he said.

'There's room, is there, in this week's column?'

'Just. All hands to the pumps and so forth.'

'I'm obliged. Surely it was Alexci Sayle . . .'

'That's the one,' said Lovering. 'April 1989, unless I'm much mistaken. The old ones are the best.'

'. . . who once said to me over lunch that Ben Elton doesn't have a sense of humour. Humour's a code, Sayle observed. Elton can recognize it, but can't crack it. So he copies it, like a dog shaking hands.'

'Thank you,' said Lovering. 'That will be all.'

I turned to go, but then a thought occurred. 'Have you finished this week's column?'

'Not yet,' said Lovering. 'After a joke or two about my not being able to find a hat to fit me, and your stuff about Ben Elton, I thought I might explore a theme that chimes quite happily with work in progress. I'm currently updating the best of my Root books, *Henry Root's World of Knowledge* – a handy anthology, you may remember, of portly British middlebrow fatuities, a modest tribute in its way to Flaubert's *Bouvard et Pécuchet*, vaguely

181

bookish waffle culled for the most part from the *Spectator* and Bernard Levin's column in . . .'

I chipped in, keen to show that I was on the ball. 'A good book,' I said, 'should be read with a glass of wine in one hand, as it will almost certainly have been written.' That was one. 'Ludwig Wittgenstein, he never appreciated that accessibility of thought is largely a question of good manners, but then he was notorious in his lifetime for his cultivated social awkwardness.'

'Thank you,' said Lovering. 'The cultural values of the country vicarage and the Garrick Club. Be that as it may, I recently came across an appropriate entry in the book pages of the *Sunday Times*. Discussing *The Letters of Samuel Johnson*, the Rt Hon. J. Enoch Powell (a past president of the Johnson Appreciation Society of Lichfield) wrote: "Dr Samuel Johnson was a lexicographer, editor of Shakespeare's plays and hack journalist. Yet he walks abroad among us today . . . etc etc."'

'Disgraceful,' I said. 'No mention of the poetry.'

'Precisely,' said Lovering. 'If you can't appreciate Johnson's verse you will fail in appreciation of his prose; and you will not be able to follow through the considerations involved in the appreciation of his talk. To those seriously interested in literature, the cult of Johnson is an exasperation and a challenge. It is a branch of good mixing, and its essential *raison d'être* is anti-highbrow. Johnson, one finds oneself having again and again to insist, was not only the Great Clubman; he was a great writer and a great highbrow. The Rt Hon. J. Enoch Powell's remarks exhibit the kind of literary accomplishment that goes with an admiration for P.G. Wodehouse and *Inspector Morse*.'

'Dr Leavis couldn't have put it better,' I said. 'Indeed, with the exception of the bit about *Inspector Morse*, he didn't put it better. You have the great man by heart, I see.'

'Before my exams at university,' said Lovering, 'I wrote his finest insights on my cuffs. I came down unhonoured, but my shirts were awarded a good 2:1.'

Should there be another series of *Root Into Europe* I'll be back in the saddle, I think, and Lovering will be upside down in a ditch.

Boots Stakes My Baby Out

I was having lunch on Monday with Michael O'Mara, the brilliant young American publisher, when he suddenly started to cry. I was shocked. O'Mara's a real man, a starting quarter-back once with the Philadelphia Eagles, and they're a blue-collar team if ever there was one.

On top of which, if anyone had a reason to cry it was me rather than O'Mara. I'd just had the worst weekend of my life, caused by Abby from the Eighties trying to make me doubt my baby. We were discussing this and that on Friday night when Abby from the Eighties gave me a funny look and said: 'Do you trust your literary agent, Alison?'

'What a silly question,' I said. 'Of course I do.'

'You know about Roger, then?'

I'd had this sort of stuff before. Roger was the love of my baby's life but she hasn't seen him for at least four years. 'Naturally,' I said. 'My guess is they live together,' said Abby from the Eighties.

I ask you. As if my beloved could have been living with someone all the time I'd known her without my twigging. In fact, she shares a house with her friend Anna. Why, then this sudden pain like dysentery in the lower bowel?

Pull the other one,' I said, but I was reaching for my brains, was wearing the uncertain silly grin an outclassed sparring partner assumes for bravado's sake just before the lights go out.

'If I were you, I'd stake her out,' said Abby from the Eighties.

I was reeling, but able for all that to recognize this as one of the most vulgar ideas I'd ever heard. An old man with his collar turned up, wet pavements, young people laughing in a brightly lit room. When trust goes, everything goes.

'I'll get my friend Boots to stake her out,' I said.

Boots has recently become a private eye and, with telephoto lens and bugging gear, will park her van outside your house, the former having a large painted sign on its side that reads: 'Boots & Co – Secret Investigations'. Rather a self-defeating slogan, in my opinion, but she'll know her business best.

We summoned her over for a briefing and then Abby from the Eighties had a sharp idea. Since my baby was spending the weekend in Norfolk with her mother, all Boots had to do was ring up Anna (who'd know my voice) and ask to speak to Roger. I felt more confident, I don't know why, while Boots dialled the number, perhaps because I'd had no premonition on waking up that morning, that I'd die on the spot at 10 p.m. – a certain outcome if Roger answered or turned out to be there. Either way, someone would be looking very silly in a minute.

'Can I speak to Roger, please?' said Boots.

'He's away for the weekend,' Anna said. 'He'll be back on Sunday night.'

I rang my beloved on Sunday evening and said that I needed urgently to see her.

'All right,' she said. 'But I can't stay long. I've got to be home for dinner.'

'Do you still see Roger?' I said as soon as she arrived at my place.

'No,' she said. 'I told you. I haven't seen him for four years.'

That was good enough for me, if not for her. She, quite rightly, was furious with me for doubting her and, as a punishment, has insisted that I send her and her father on a skiing holiday in France. This won't be cheap which is why it hit me suddenly, in the course of lunch on Monday with Mike O'Mara, that I needed to sell him something rather urgently. Easier said than done. O'Mara is one of the nicest men you could hope to meet, but he didn't just ride into town with his trousers held up with harvest twine. In the normal course of things I wouldn't even try to slip one past him, but today he wasn't himself. His face was puffy with grief and he spoke in a low, hesitant quaver. It's an ill wind and so forth. I could take him easily.

'Stop crying, for goodness' sake,' I said.

'I'm not crying,' he said. 'It's an allergy. I was sneezing all night. I didn't get a wink of sleep.'

Whatever. He was in bad shape which was all that mattered.

'Here's one,' I said. 'You bring out my collected columns from the *Independent* as a book!'

'That's a terrible idea,' he said. 'No one would buy that.'

'You're right,' I said. I was quite cast down, but I rallied quickly. 'How about this, though? We call it *Root Into Europe*. A TV tie-in.'

O'Mara looked quite shocked. Perhaps he wasn't in such bad

shape after all. 'That would be fraud,' he said.

'Perhaps you're right,' I said. 'But you're forgetting something. The serialization rights in my collected columns would be worth a bomb.'

'I don't know,' said O'Mara. 'Who could we sell them to?'

'The *Independent*, of course,' I said.

'You're on,' said O'Mara.

There's one born every minute. My literary agent, Alison, shall have a summer holiday in Monaco as well.

J.J.'s Christmas Humour List

Unfortunately, Michael O'Mara has recovered from the nasty allergy that struck him down last week (he felt so dicky, you may remember, that he agreed to bring out a selection of these columns as a book) and, as a consequence, I am to be published in future not by him but by his boy, J.J.

Confident that I could slip six more proposals past him if his condition hadn't improved, I pitched up for lunch on Wednesday only to discover he was back on form: bright-eyed and apple-cheeked, cracking his knuckles menacingly and swaying backwards and forwards on the balls of his feet like the fistfighter he once had been.

'Still a little under the weather?' I said. 'Walking into walls? Weeping mysteriously like a woman? Here's one . . .'

I was clutching at straws, such was the urgency of the situation. Alison, my beloved, had been displeased by certain revelations about her private life in last week's column and, by way of compensation, had demanded a sunshine break in the Seychelles with her father, as well as the skiing holiday in France.

'On the contrary,' O'Mara said. 'I'm quite myself again and in the nick of time. After your piece appeared every deluded person in the land sent me the contents of his bottom drawer. Vicars. Provincial solicitors. Burly, householding women from the home counties. Marine architects on a pension, now resident in Bath. Squinting with pain from my blocked sinuses, and dizzy from lack of sleep, I agreed on Monday to publish the memoirs of a

185

country curate who, for reasons of his own, pushed a wheel-barrow across the Kalahari desert and recorded his adventures on the way – not that he had any.'

'Hardly my fault,' I said.

'There's worse,' O'Mara said. 'By the end of the day I had, in addition, agreed to publish illustrated toilet books by six comedians. The big one, the black one, the fat one . . .'

O'Mara groaned and clutched his forehead. I cheered up slightly, imagining for a moment that he was about to suffer a relapse, but he pulled himself together.

'And the other one,' he said.

'The other one's the worst,' I said.

'You're telling me,' he said. 'At that point, luckily, I discovered what was causing my condition. I sneezed for most of Monday night and then I realized that I must be allergic to something on the pillow. I got up and padded softly into J.J.'s room.'

'How old is J.J.?' I asked.

'Five,' O'Mara said.

'Bless him,' I said.

'Never mind bless him,' O'Mara said. 'I removed J.J.'s pillow from under his head and, without waking him, substituted mine – the one that causes the sneezing attacks.'

'Poor J.J.,' I said. 'So now he's sneezing all night?'

'Worse,' O'Mara said. 'On Tuesday he announced his Christmas humour list – An Explosion of Hilarity from J.J. O'Mara! – the first title being *Oops! Silly Me! – Hilarious Mishaps on the Home Front!* by Maureen Lipman.'

'Oh dear,' I said. 'But you're all right now?'

'I thought so,' O'Mara said. 'But on Tuesday I sneezed all night again, and on Wednesday I commissioned a novel by Tony Slattery, and *Ballots and Elections! Try Saying That in a Chinese Restaurant! Hilarious Bloopers on the Hustings* by Gyles Brandreth and Bill Oddie.'

'How come?'

'J.J. isn't as silly as he looks,' O'Mara said. 'When he retired to bed on Tuesday evening he noticed his Thomas the Tank pillow was missing. He went into our bedroom and discovered the exchange. He recovered his pillow and replaced it with the one that makes you sneeze. I didn't notice this when I went to bed – hence my bad night. Now I've swapped again and, as you can see

186

for yourself, I'm as right as nine pence, but on Thursday J.J. commissioned *Now is the Winter of Our Discount Tents! Camp Tales from the Sales!* by Julian Clary.'

'No chance, then, of your publishing my . . .'

'None at all,' O'Mara said.

This was serious, since I needed urgently to raise the wind. Alison had come round on Sunday night, without her legs and in a rage, and very rude she'd been. I don't like that. A woman should be elusive – pouting and treacherous and, when you most need her, thrillingly occupied elsewhere – but she shouldn't be rude. Nor should she demand a holiday in the Seychelles when wearing trousers and flat-heeled shoes. If you want trousers and flat-heeled shoes you might as well make your arrangements with a man and have your shirts done properly. I'd told her to apologize.

'I'm ever so sorry, Mr Mouse,' she'd said. 'Can I go to the Seychelles, then?'

I thought now of her little hands, her unconsoling eyes, her witty infidelities and I returned to the attack.

'Any chance of J.J. commissioning a couple of books?' I said.

'Possibly,' O'Mara said. 'If you take him to the zoo first.'

This has been arranged for Sunday, so keep your fingers crossed.

Mind the Gibbon

I gather from an election special that, depending on which party wins, the better off are to be worse off and the worse off better off by as much as £1.78 a week. There's food for thought here, obviously, and all but the incorrigibly feckless would be well advised to cast their votes accordingly.

My difficulty is that from the age of six, when I became financially independent (trust funds, estates in Scotland, my own shipping line and so forth), it has been unclear to me from day to day in which category – the well off or the worse off – I properly belong.

How is one supposed to know? On days when a scheme bears

fruit one is quids in, clearly, but on others one finds oneself without the funds to pick the laundry up. Three weeks ago, for instance, I was boasting here that, as a consequence of my entry into the music business, I'd be off-shore by Easter, eating chicken on Sunday and wearing elastic-sided boots. Yet, by this weekend, I was obliged to tap a five-year-old (Michael O'Mara's boy, J.J., to be precise) for marching money; more accurately, for the price of a sunshine break in the Seychelles for my baby and her father – the penalty I had to pay for doubting her, for being so common as to suggest that, just because she'd been living with a man all the time I'd known her, she'd been living with him, so to speak.

I took young J.J., to the zoo on Sunday and, since time was of the essence, I came straight to the point – confident, I may say, that I'd shake him down with ease. In the old days at the Ivy, and keen to fund a musical, I'd separated harder men than young J.J. from their unearnt incomes and none, as I remember, had brought Mr Poo the Panda with him.

'You're liquid, are you?' I said. 'At least, have trust funds handy? A visit, perhaps, to executors in chambers. Doff the bowler, shoot the cuff: "Morning, Dilhorne. Kindly spring a wedge from the Scottish Widows for Mr Donaldson here. I've commissioned him to write a clutch of illustrated toilet books for my Christmas Humour List." My word, I could do with a jumbo-burger and a banana milkshake. Mr Poo feeling a little peckish, by any chance? Mind the moose.'

My baby's sunshine break was in the bag. O'Mara would have made provision for J.J., just as my father had for me. 'Ah, there you are,' my father had said, appearing unexpectedly in my quarters one day when I was six. 'William, is it? I'm your father. Here's a cheque for £100,000. Don't spend it all at once. I'll be off now.'

'It isn't a moose,' J.J. said. 'It's a North American bison. And I've only got threepence on me. My father gives me ten shillings a week, but I prefer not to carry large sums about my person. So you'll have to get the jumbo-burgers. Nor, I may say, is Mr Poo feeling peckish. He isn't a *real* panda, he's a *toy* panda. So let's not have any more of that sentimental rubbish.'

I'd got one here. When I was a businessman, I did the buying, wore an overcoat and took satirists out to lunch, but times had changed, it seemed. I didn't give up yet, however. If I could bring J.J.'s allergy back by sprinkling pepper on his jumbo-burger, the day could yet be saved.

'Watch your back!' I said. 'There's a gibbon coming up behind you.'

'Oh yes?' said J.J. 'And while I'm distracted, you sprinkle pepper on my jumbo-burger. You'd do better at your age to offer some worldly wisdom. You must have learnt something in the course of a long life.'

'I have, as it happens,' I said. 'Never listen to anyone who is stupider than you are — not least when they know what they are talking about. Equally, you should blindly follow those who are obviously cleverer, particularly when you can't understand a word they say. Put it this way: were Jonathan Miller to watch a game of American football, his comments would, clearly, be of greater interest than mine; well, not mine, perhaps, but certainly than anyone else's. The idea came to me this week. Justin Judd had just let me see the first two episodes of *Root Into Europe*, but he wouldn't let me keep the tape.'

'Why not?' said J.J.

'He was concerned that I'd show it to my pseudo-intellectual friends. But why would I have done that? Pseudo-intellectuals (the next best thing, obviously, to proper intellectuals) are indeed the only people whose opinions interest me but, since nothing could now be changed, a negative judgement from them would merely have depressed me. Judd found this attitude élitist. He is extremely intelligent himself, you understand, but he hasn't yet learnt that what the man on the Clapham omnibus thinks is neither here nor there — a fatal mistake for a producer to make. By the time I was your age, young J.J., I had produced fifteen West End entertainments and I'm proud to say that I never listened to anyone who said: "But will the man from Cleethorpes understand?"'

'How did they do?' J.J. said.

'Flops, the lot of them,' I said. 'Disgusting failures. Débâcles. Outrages. Are you listening?'

'No,' he said. 'I've decided that you're stupider than I am. Mind the gibbon.'